7

Show What You Know® on the

MSP

Preparation for the Measurements of Student Progress
Washington Comprehensive Assessment Program

Name: _____

Published by:

Show What You Know® Publishing
A Division of Englefield & Associates, Inc.
P.O. Box 341348
Columbus, OH 43234-1348
Phone: 614-764-1211
www.showwhatyouknowpublishing.com
www.passtheMSP.com

MSP information was obtained from the Office of Superintendent of Public Instruction Web site, August 2009.

Printed in the United States of America
11 10 09   20 19 18 17 16 15 14 13 12 11 10 9 8 7 6 5 4 3 2 1

ISBN: 1-59230-344-7

Table of Contents

Acknowledgements

Show What You Know® Publishing acknowledges the following for their efforts in making this assessment material available for Washington students, parents, and teachers:

Cindi Englefield, President/Publisher
Eloise Boehm-Sasala, Vice President/Managing Editor
Christine Filippetti, Production Editor
Jill Borish, Production Editor
Jennifer Harney, Editor/Illustrator

About the Contributors

The content of this book was written BY teachers FOR teachers and students and was designed specifically for the Measurements of Student Progress (MSP) for Grade 7. Contributions to the Writing, Reading, and Mathematics sections of this book were also made by the educational publishing staff at Show What You Know® Publishing. Dr. Jolie S. Brams, a clinical child and family psychologist, is the contributing author of the Test Anxiety and Test-Taking Strategies chapters of this book. Without the contributions of these people, this book would not be possible.

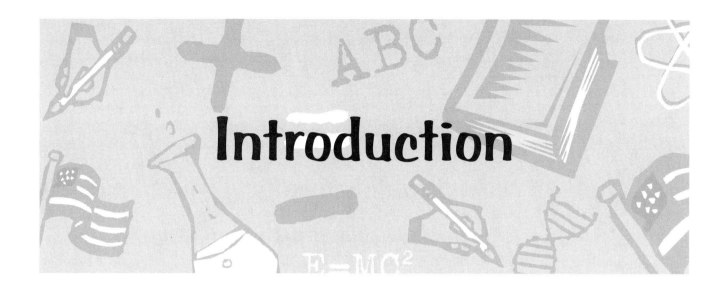

Introduction

Dear Student:

This *Show What You Know® on the MSP for Grade 7, Student Workbook* was created to give you lots of practice in preparation for the Measurements of Student Progress (MSP) in Writing, Reading, and Mathematics.

The first two chapters in this workbook—Test Anxiety and Test-Taking Strategies—were written especially for seventh-grade students. Test Anxiety offers advice on how to get rid of the bad feelings you may have about tests. The Test-Taking Strategies chapter gives you examples of the kinds of questions you will see on the MSP, such as multiple choice, completion items, and short-answer questions and includes helpful tips on how to answer these questions correctly so you can succeed on the MSP.

The next two chapters of this Student Workbook help you prepare for the Writing, Reading, and Mathematics MSP.
- The Writing chapter includes a Writing Practice Tutorial, a Writing Assessment, and a Writing Glossary of terms that will help you show what you know on the MSP.
- The Reading chapter includes a Reading Practice Tutorial, two full-length Reading Assessments, and a Reading Glossary of terms that will help you show what you know on the MSP.
- The Mathematics chapter includes a Mathematics Practice Tutorial, a full-length Mathematics Assessment, a Glossary of Mathematics Terms, and a Glossary of Mathematical Illustrations that will help you show what you know on the MSP.

This Student Workbook will help you become familiar with the look and feel of the MSP and will provide you with a chance to practice your test-taking skills to show what you know.

Good luck on the MSP!

This page intentionally left blank.

Test Anxiety

What is Test Anxiety?

Test anxiety is just a fancy name for feeling nervous about tests. Everyone knows what it is like to be nervous. Feeling nervous is not a good experience.

Many students have anxiety about taking tests, so if you are a test worrier, don't let it worry you. Most likely, many of your fellow students and friends also have fearful feelings about tests but do not share these feelings with others. Seventh grade is a time when everyone wants to seem "grown up," and few seventh graders want to look weak or afraid in the eyes of their friends or their teachers. But not talking to others about anxiety only makes the situation worse. It makes you feel alone and also makes you wonder if there is something "wrong" with you. Be brave. Talk to your friends and teachers about test anxiety. You will feel better for sharing.

What Does It Feel Like to Have Test Anxiety?

Students who have test anxiety don't always feel the same way, but they always feel bad. Here are some ways that students feel when they are anxious about tests.

- **Students who have test anxiety rarely think good things about themselves.**
  They lack confidence in their abilities, and they are convinced they will do poorly on tests. Not only do they feel bad about themselves and their abilities, but they just can't keep negative thoughts out of their minds. They would probably make terrible detectives, because in spite of all the good things they could find out about themselves, they only think about what they can't do. And that's not the worst of it. Students with test anxiety also exaggerate. When they think of the smallest problem, it becomes a hundred times bigger, especially when they think about tests. They are very unforgiving of themselves. If they make a mistake, they always think the worst or exaggerate the situation. If they do poorly on a quiz, they never say, "Well, it's just a quiz, and I'll do better next time." Instead they think, "That test was terrible and I can only imagine how badly I'll do next week." For students with test anxiety, there is never a brighter day ahead. They don't think many good thoughts about themselves, and they certainly don't have a happy outlook on their lives.

- **Students who have test anxiety have poor "thinking habits."**
  Negative thinking is a habit just like any other habit. Some habits are good and some habits are bad, but negative thinking is probably the worst habit of all. A habit forms when you do something over and over again until it becomes so much a part of you that you don't think about it anymore. Students with test anxiety get into bad habits of thinking. They develop negative ways of thinking about themselves and about schoolwork, especially about tests. They tend to make the worst out of situations and imagine all kinds of possibilities that probably will not happen. Their thoughts grow like a mushroom out of control. Besides having negative ideas about tests, they begin to have negative ideas about almost everything else in their lives. This is not a good way of thinking because the more poorly they feel about themselves, the worse they do in school, and bad grades make them feel even worse about themselves. What a mess. Students who have constant negative thoughts about themselves and schoolwork probably have test anxiety.

- **Students who have test anxiety may feel physically uncomfortable or even ill.**

  It is important to know that your mind and body are connected. What goes on in your mind can change how your body feels, and how your body feels can influence what goes on in your thinking. When students have test anxiety, their thoughts might cause them to have physical symptoms which include a fast heartbeat, butterflies in the stomach, headaches, and all sorts of other physical problems. Some kids become so ill they end up going to the doctor because they believe they are truly sick. Some students miss a lot of school due to anxiety, but they aren't really ill. Instead, their thoughts are controlling their bodies in a negative way. Some anxious students do not realize that what they are feeling is anxiety. They miss many days of school, not because they are lazy or neglectful, but because they believe they truly are not feeling well. Unfortunately, the more school they miss, the more behind they are and the more nervous they feel. Students who suffer from test anxiety probably feel even worse on test days. Their uncomfortable physical feelings will make them either avoid the test completely or feel so bad during the test that they do poorly. Guess what happens then. They feel even worse about themselves, become more anxious, and the cycle goes on and on.

- **Students who have test anxiety "freak out" and want to escape.**

  Many students feel so bad when they are anxious that they will do anything to avoid that feeling. For most students, this means running away from problems, especially tests. Some students try to get away from tests by missing school. This does not solve any problems; the more a student is away from school, the harder schoolwork is and the worse he or she feels. Some students worry about being worried. It may sound silly, but they are worried that they are going to freak out, and guess what happens . . . they do. They are so terrified that they will have uncontrollable anxious feelings that they actually get anxious feelings when thinking about this problem. For many students, anxiety is such a bad feeling that they will do anything not to feel anxious, even if it means failing tests or school. Although they know this will cause them problems in the future, their anxiety is so overwhelming they would rather avoid anxiety now and fail later. Unfortunately, this is usually what happens.

- **Students who have test anxiety do not show what they know on tests.**

  Students who have test anxiety do not make good decisions on tests. Instead of focusing their thoughts, planning out their answers, and using what they know, students find themselves "blanking out." They stare at the paper, and no answer is there. They become "stuck" and cannot move on. Some students come up with the wrong answers because their anxiety gets in the way of reading directions carefully and thinking about answers thoughtfully. Their minds are running in a hundred different ways and none of those ways seem to be getting them anywhere. They forget to use what they know, and they also forget to use study skills that can help students do their best. When students are so worried that they cannot make good decisions and use all of the talents they have, it is called test anxiety.

Are You One of These "Test-Anxious" Seventh Graders?

As you have seen, students with test anxiety have negative thoughts about themselves, often feel anxious to the point of being ill, freak out and want to escape, and rarely show what they know on tests. Do any of the following kids remind you of yourself?

Stay-Away Stephanie

Stephanie's thoughts tell her it is better to stay away from challenges, especially tests. Stephanie is a good girl, but she is always in trouble at school for avoiding tests. Sometimes, she really feels ill and begs her mom to allow her to stay home on test days. At other times, Stephanie does anything to avoid school, refusing to get up in the morning or to leave the house to catch the bus. Stephanie truly believes there is nothing worse than taking a test. She is so overwhelmed with anxiety that she forgets about the problems that will happen when she stays away from her responsibilities. Unfortunately, the more she stays away, the worse the situation becomes. Stay-Away Stephanie feels less nervous when she doesn't face a test, but she never learns to face her fears.

Worried Wendy

Wendy is the type of seventh grader who always expects the worst thing to happen. She has many negative thoughts. Even when situations have turned out to be OK, Wendy focuses on the few bad things that happened. She exaggerates negative events and forgets about everything good. Her mind races a mile a minute with all sorts of thoughts and ideas about tests. The more she thinks,

the worse she feels, and her problems become unbelievably huge. Instead of just worrying about a couple of difficult questions on a test, she finds herself thinking about failing the whole test, being made fun of by her friends, being grounded by her parents, and never going to college. She completely forgets that her parents would never be so strict, that her friends like her for many more reasons than her test grades, and that she has all sorts of career choices ahead of her. No one is going to hold it against her if she performs poorly on a test. It is not going to ruin her life. However, Wendy believes all of that would happen. Her negative thoughts get in the way of thinking anything positive.

Critical Chris

Chris is the type of seventh grader who spends all of his time putting himself down. No matter what happens, he always feels he has been a failure. While some people hold grudges against others, Chris holds grudges against himself. No matter what little mistakes he makes, he can never forget them. Chris has had many good things happen to him in his life, and he has been successful many times. Unfortunately, Chris forgets all the good and only remembers the bad. Because he doesn't appreciate himself, Chris has test anxiety.

Victim Vince

Most seventh graders find it is important to take responsibility for their actions. It helps them understand that adulthood is just around the corner, and that they are smarter and more able than they ever thought they were. However, Vince is not like this. He can't take responsibility for himself at all. He thinks everything is someone else's fault and constantly complains about friends, parents, schoolwork, and especially tests. He tells himself, "They make those tests too hard." He sees the teachers as unfair, and he thinks life is generally against him. Vince does not feel there is anything he can do to help his situation, and there is little he thinks he can do to help himself with tests. Because he does not try to learn test-taking skills or to understand why he is afraid, he continues to feel hopeless and angry. Not surprisingly, he does poorly on tests, which only makes his thoughts about the world around him worse.

Perfect Pat

Everyone knows that there is more homework and responsibility in seventh grade than in previous grades. Everyone in the seventh grade needs to try his or her best, but no one should try as much as Pat does. All Pat does is worry. No matter what she does, it's never good enough. She will write book reports over and over and study for tests until she is exhausted. Trying hard is fine, but no matter what Pat does, she feels she has never done enough. Because she never accomplishes what she sets out to do (that would be impossible), she worries all the time. Her anxiety level gets higher and higher. The more anxious she becomes, the worse she does on tests. This just makes her study and worry more. What a terrible situation!

How Do I Handle Test Anxiety?

Test anxiety is a very powerful feeling that convinces students they are weak and helpless. Feelings of test anxiety can be so powerful it seems there is nothing you can do to stop them. Anxiety seems to take over your mind and body and leaves you feeling like you are going to lose the test anxiety battle for sure.

The good news is that there are many simple things you can do to win the battle over test anxiety. If you can learn these skills in the seventh grade, you are on the road to success in school and for all other challenges in your life.

- **Change the way you think.**
  Most of us don't "think about how we think." We just go along thinking our thoughts and never really considering whether they are helpful or not helpful or if they are right or wrong. We rarely realize how much the way we think has to do with how well we get along in life. Our thoughts can influence how we feel about ourselves, how we get along with other people, how well we do in school, and how we perform on tests.

- **The Soda Pop Test.**
  Most seventh graders have heard a parent or teacher tell them, "There is more than one side to any story." One student reported that his grandfather used to say, "There's more than one way to paint a fence." Have you ever considered how you think about different situations? Most situations can be looked at in many ways, both good and bad.

Take a can of soda pop and put it on your desk or dresser at home. Get out a piece of paper and a pen or a pencil. Now, draw a line down the middle of the paper. On one side, put a heading: "All the bad things about this can of soda pop." On the other side, put another heading: "All the good things about this can of soda pop." If you think about that can of soda pop, you might come up with the following chart:

All the bad things about this can of soda pop	All the good things about this can of soda pop
Not an attractive color	Easy-to-read lettering
It's getting warm	Nice to have something to drink
Not much in the can	Inexpensive
Has a lot of sugar	Recyclable aluminum cans

Look how easy it is to write down good things or bad things about a silly can of soda pop. That can of soda pop is not really good or bad, it's just a can of soda pop, but we can either look at it in a positive way or we can think about everything negative that comes to our minds. Doesn't the same thing hold true for tests? Tests are not good or bad in themselves. Tests are just a way to challenge us and see what we know. Challenges can be stressful, but they can also be rewarding. Studying for tests can be boring and can take up a lot of free time, but we can also learn a lot and feel great about ourselves when we study. The way you think about tests will help determine how you do in a test-taking situation. Most importantly, how you feel about tests is related to your level of anxiety about test taking. Students who have negative thoughts and feelings about tests become anxious. Students who think positively are less anxious. To reduce test anxiety, try thinking about tests and testing situations using a positive frame of mind.

- **All or Nothing Thinking.**
Nothing is ever as simple as it seems. Sometimes we convince ourselves something is going to be "awful" or "wonderful." Rarely does it turn out that way.

Trouble comes along when students think tests are going to be an "awful" experience. If you dread something happening, it is only going to make things worse. Also, you may be wrong. Nothing is as terrible as it seems. All the negative thoughts you have about the upcoming test cannot possibly be true. Thinking something is "awful" or "terrible" and nothing else only leads to trouble and failure. The more negative you feel about something, the worse things turn out.

Very few things are "all good" or "all bad." This is especially true for tests. Recognizing the "bad" parts of tests can help you be successful. For example, the fact that you need to study for tests, to pay attention while you are taking tests, and to understand there are probably many more fun things to do in school than take tests are all "true" thoughts. "Good" thoughts are just as true, including the good feelings one gets from studying and the chance that you might do well. Having "all or nothing" thinking is going to get you nowhere. Successful and happy students know some experiences are better than others, but they try to look at a situation from all sides.

- **Mind Reading.**
Some students believe they can read the minds of their parents and teachers. They assume if they do poorly on the MSP, everyone will think they are "dumb" or "lazy." The more their minds create all the terrible things that people may say about them, the more anxious they get. This just increases anxiety and definitely does not help students do well on tests.

- **Catastrophizing.**

  When people catastrophize, they make everything a catastrophe. A catastrophe is a disaster. It is when something terrible happens. When a student catastrophizes, his or her mind goes on and on creating terrible scenes of disasters. If someone put all these ideas into a movie script, the writer might be rich.

  The MSP is an important part of a seventh-grader's school year. It is a test that helps the student, the teacher, and the school. However, a seventh-grade student is much more than just his or her score on the MSP. Each student is an individual who has his or her own great personality, talents, and other successes in school. If what people catastrophized about was really true, the whole world would be a terrible mess. Imagine if your mother cooked a dinner that didn't turn out quite right. This might mean everyone has to go out for fast food, but you wouldn't love your mother any less. It would be catastrophizing if your mother said, "Now that I burned the dinner, none of my kids will love me. They will probably just want to move out as quickly as they can, and my life will be ruined." Catastrophizing about the MSP is just as bad. Thinking that this test is going to be the worst experience of your life and that your future will be ruined will not help you feel comfortable when preparing for and taking the test.

- **Making "Should" Statements.**

  Students make themselves anxious when they think they "should" do everything. They feel they "should" be as smart as everyone else, "should" study more, and "should" not feel anxious about tests. All these thoughts are pretty ridiculous. You can't always be as smart as the next person, and you do not have to study until you drop to do well on tests. Instead of kicking yourself for not being perfect, it is better to think about all the good things you have done in your life. This will help you do better on tests and be happier in your life by reducing your anxiety.

How Do I Replace Worried Thoughts with Positive Ones?

As we have learned, there are all kinds of thoughts that make us anxious, such as feeling we "should" do everything, thinking we can read peoples' minds, catastrophizing, and thinking only bad thoughts about a situation. Learning how to stop these types of thoughts is very important. Understanding your thoughts and doing something about them will help you control test anxiety.

People who are worried or anxious can become happier when thinking positive thoughts. Even when situations are scary, such as a visit to the dentist, "positive imagery" is helpful. "Positive imagery" means thinking good thoughts to keep from thinking anxious thoughts. Positive and negative thoughts do not go together. If you are thinking something positive, it is almost impossible to think of something negative. Keep this in mind when test anxiety starts to become a bother.

Try these ideas the next time you find yourself becoming anxious.

- **Thoughts of Success.**
  Thinking "I can do it" thoughts can chase away thoughts of failure. Imagine times you were successful, such as when you performed well in a dance recital or figured out a complicated brain teaser. These are good things to think about. Telling yourself you have been successful in the past and can be successful in the future will chase away thoughts of anxiety.

- **Relaxing Thoughts.**
  Some people find that thinking calming or relaxing thoughts is helpful. Picturing a time in which you felt comfortable and happy can lessen your anxious feelings. Imagine yourself playing a baseball game, running through a park, or eating an ice cream cone; these are all positive thoughts that may get in the way of anxious ones. Some students find that listening to music on the morning of a test is helpful. It probably doesn't matter what music you listen to, as long as it makes you feel good about yourself, confident, and relaxed.

  Just as you can calm your mind, it is also important for you to relax your body. Practice relaxing your body. When students have test anxiety, their muscles become stiff. In fact, the whole body becomes tense. Taking deep breaths before a test and letting them out slowly as well as relaxing muscles in your body are all very helpful ways to feel less anxious. Your school counselors will probably have more ideas about relaxation. You may find that relaxation doesn't just help you on tests, but is helpful for other challenging situations and for feeling healthy overall.

- **Don't Let Yourself Feel Alone.**
  Everyone feels more anxious when they feel alone and separate from others. Talking to your friends, parents, and teachers about your feelings helps. Feeling anxious about tests does not mean there is something wrong with you. You will be surprised to find that many of your friends and fellow students also feel anxious about tests. You may be even more surprised to learn your parents and teachers have also had test anxiety. They know what you are going through and are there to support you.

- **Take Care of Yourself.**
Everyone is busy. Many seventh graders are involved in all sorts of activities, including sports, music, and helping around the house. Often, you are so busy you forget to eat breakfast or you don't get enough sleep. Eating and sleeping right are important, especially before a test like the MSP. If you are not a big breakfast eater, try to find something that you like to eat and get in the habit of eating breakfast. When you do not eat right, you may feel shaky and have a hard time concentrating, and your anxiety can increase. Being tired does not help either. Try to get in the habit of going to bed at a good time every night (especially the night before a test) so you can feel fresh, rested, and confident for the MSP.

- **Practice Your Test-Taking Success.**
People who have accomplished incredibly difficult goals have used their imaginations to help them achieve success. They thought about what they would do step by step to be successful.

  You can do the same. Think about yourself on the morning of the test. Imagine telling yourself positive thoughts and eating a good breakfast. Think about arriving at school and feeling confident that you will do fine on the test. Imagine closing your eyes before the test, breathing deeply, relaxing, and remembering all the study skills you have learned. The more you program your mind to think in a successful and positive way, the better off you will be.

- **Learn to Use Study Skills.**
The next chapter in this book will help you learn test-taking strategies. The more you know about taking tests successfully, the calmer you will feel. Knowledge is power. Practice test-taking strategies to reduce your test anxiety.

- **Congratulate Yourself During the Test.**
Instead of thinking, "I've only done five problems and I've got eight pages to go," or "I knew three answers were right, but one mixed me up," reward yourself for what you have done. Tell yourself, "I got some answers right so far, so I bet I can do more." After all, if you don't compliment yourself, who will?

Conclusion

You are not alone if you feel stressed about tests. It is probably good to feel a little anxious, because it motivates you to do well. However, if you feel very anxious about tests, then reading, re-reading, and practicing the suggestions in this chapter will help you tackle your test anxiety.

Test-Taking Strategies

All Students Can Do Their Best on Tests!

Most students want to do their best on tests. Tests are one important way for teachers to know how well students are doing and for students to understand how much progress they are making in their studies. Tests like the MSP help schools measure how well students are learning so teachers and principals can make their schools even better. Students can do the best job possible in "showing what they know" by learning how to be good test takers.

It's just not possible to do a good job without the right tools. Test-taking strategies are tools to help you perform well on tests. Everyone needs good tools and strategies when facing a problem. If you do not have these, even the smartest or most talented person will do poorly. Think about people who are wizards at fixing cars and trucks. Your family's car dies in the middle of the road. The situation looks pretty hopeless. How are you ever going to get to that basketball game tomorrow if your parent's car is a mechanical mess? Suddenly, magic happens. The technician at the repair shop calls your parents and tells them the car is ready, just a day after it broke down. How did this happen? It happened because the auto-repair technician had a great deal of knowledge about cars. Most importantly, he had the right tools and strategies to fix the car. He knew how to look at the problem, and when he figured out what to do, he had some special gadgets to get the job done. You also can find special ways that will help you be a successful test taker.

Tools You Can Use on the MSP and Tests Throughout Your Life!

Be An "Active Learner."

You can't learn anything by being a "sponge." Just because you are sitting in a pool of learning (your classroom) does not mean you are going to learn anything just by being there. Instead, students learn when they actively think and participate during the school day. Students who are active learners pay attention to what is being said. They also constantly ask themselves and their teachers questions about the subject. When able, they participate by making comments and joining discussions. Active learners enjoy school, learn more, feel good about themselves, and usually do better on tests. Remember the auto-repair technician? That person had a lot of knowledge about fixing cars. All the tools and strategies in the world will not help unless you have benefited from what your teachers have tried to share.

Being an active learner takes time and practice. If you are the type of student who is easily bored or frustrated, it is going to take some practice to use your classroom time differently. Ask yourself the following questions.

• Am I looking at the teacher?

• Do I pay attention to what is being said?

• Do I have any questions or ideas about what the teacher is saying?

• Do I listen to what my fellow students are saying and think about their ideas?

• Do I work with others to try to solve difficult problems?

• Do I look at the clock and wonder what time school will be over, or do I appreciate what is happening during the school day and how much I can learn?

• Do I try to think about how my schoolwork might be helpful to me now or in the future?

Although you do need special tools and strategies to do well on tests, the more you learn, the better chance you have of doing well on tests. Think about Kristen.

There was a young girl named Kristen,
Who was bored and wouldn't listen.
She didn't train
To use her smart brain
And never knew what she was missing!

Don't Depend on Luck.
Preparing for the MSP might feel stressful or boring at times, but it is an important part of learning how to show what you know and doing your best. Even the smartest student needs to spend time taking practice tests and listening to the advice of teachers about how to do well. Luck alone is not going to help you do well on the MSP or other tests. People who depend on luck do not take responsibility for themselves. Some people who believe in luck do not want to take the time and effort to do well. It is easier for them to say, "It's not my fault I did poorly. It's just not my lucky day." Some people just do not feel very good about their abilities. They get in the habit of saying, "Whatever happens will happen." They believe they can never do well no matter how much they practice or prepare. Students who feel they have no control over what happens to them usually have poor grades and do not feel very good about themselves.

Your performance on the MSP (and other tests) is not going to be controlled by luck. Instead, you can have a lot of control over how well you do in many areas of your life, including test taking. Don't be like Chuck.

There was a cool boy named Chuck,
Who thought taking tests was just luck.
He never prepared.
He said, "I'm not scared."
When his test score appears, he should duck!

Do Your Best Every Day.
Many students find seventh grade much different than other grades. Suddenly, the work seems really hard. Not only that, but your teachers are no longer treating you like a baby. That's good in some ways, because it gives you more freedom and responsibility, but there sure is a lot to learn. You might feel the same way about the MSP; you may feel you'll never be prepared. Many times when we are faced with new challenges, it is easy just to give up.

Students are surprised when they find that if they just set small goals for themselves, they can learn an amazing amount. If you learn just one new fact every day of the year, at the end of the year, you will know 365 new facts. You could use those to impress your friends and family. Now think about what would happen if you learned three new facts every day. At the end of the year, you would have learned 1,095 new facts. Soon you will be on your way to having a mind like an encyclopedia.

When you think about the MSP or any other academic challenge, try to focus on what you can learn step by step and day by day. You will be surprised how all of this learning adds up to make you one of the smartest seventh graders ever. Think about Ray.

There was a smart boy named Ray,
Who learned something new every day.
He was pretty impressed
With what his mind could possess.
His excellent scores were his pay!

Get to Know the MSP.
Most seventh graders are probably pretty used to riding in their parents' cars. They know how to make the air-conditioning cooler or warmer, how to change the radio stations, and how to adjust the volume on the radio. Think about being a passenger in a totally unfamiliar car. You might think, "What are all those buttons? How do I even turn on the air conditioner? How do I make the window go up and down?" Now, think about taking the MSP. The MSP is a test, but it may be different than some tests you have taken in the past. The more familiar you are with the types of questions on the MSP and how to record your answers, the better you will do. Working through the Writing, Reading, and Mathematics chapters in this book will help you get to know the MSP. Becoming familiar with the MSP is a great test-taking tool. Think about Sue.

There was a kid named Sue,
Who thought her test looked new.
"I never saw this before!
How'd I get a bad score?"
If she practiced, she might have a clue!

Read Directions and Questions Carefully!

One of the worst mistakes a student can make on the MSP is to ignore directions or to read questions carelessly. By the time some students are in the seventh grade, they think they have heard every direction or question ever invented, and it is easy for them to "tune out" directions. Telling yourself, "These directions are just like other directions," or "I'm not really going to take time to read this question because I know what the question will be," are not good test-taking strategies. It is impossible to do well on the MSP without knowing what is being asked.

Reading directions and questions slowly, repeating them to yourself, and asking yourself if what you are reading makes sense are powerful test-taking strategies. Think about Fred.

There was a nice boy named Fred,
Who forgot almost all that he read.
The directions were easy,
But he said, "I don't need these."
He should have read them instead.

Know How to Fill in Those Answer Bubbles!

Most seventh graders have taken tests that ask them to fill in answer bubbles. You might be a very bright seventh grader, but you will never "show what you know" unless you fill in the answer bubbles correctly. Don't forget: a computer will be "reading" your multiple-choice question answers. If you do not fill in the answer bubble darkly or if you use a check mark or dot instead of a dark mark, your smart thinking will not be counted. Look at the examples given below.

Correct: ●   Incorrect: ✓ ✗ ● ◖ ◑

Practice filling in the answer bubbles here: ○   ○   ○   ○   ○   ○

Learning how to fill in answer bubbles takes practice, practice, and more practice. It may not be how you are used to answering multiple-choice questions, but it is the only way to give a right answer on the MSP. Think about Kay!

A stubborn girl named Kay
Liked to answer in her own way.
Her marked answer bubbles
Gave her all sorts of troubles.
Her test scores ruined her day!

Speeding Through the Test Doesn't Help.

Most students have more than enough time to read and answer all the questions on the MSP. There will always be some students who finish the test more quickly than others, but this does not mean the test was easier for them or their answers are correct. Whether you finish at a faster rate or at a slower rate than other students in your class is not important. As long as you take your time, are well prepared, concentrate on the test, and use some of the skills in this book, you should be able to do just fine. You will not get a better score just because you finish the test before everyone else. Speeding through a test item or through the whole MSP does not help you do well. In fact, students do their best when they work at a medium rate of speed, not too slow and not too fast. Students who work too slowly tend to get worried about their answers and sometimes change correct answers into incorrect ones. Students who work too fast often make careless mistakes, and many of them do not read directions or questions carefully. Think about Liz.

There was a seventh grader named Liz,
Who sped through her test like a whiz.
She thought she should race
At a very fast pace,
But it caused her to mess up her quiz.

Answer Every Question.

There is no reason that you should not attempt to answer every question you encounter on the MSP. Even if you don't know the answer, there are ways for you to increase your chances of choosing the correct response. Use the helpful strategies described below to help you answer every question to the best of your ability.

- **If you don't know the answer, guess.**

  Did you know that on the MSP there is no penalty for guessing? That is really good news. That means you have a one out of four chance of getting a multiple-choice question right, even if you just close your eyes and guess. That means that for every four questions you guess, you should get about 25% (1 out of 4) of the questions right. Guessing alone is not going to make you a star on the MSP, but leaving multiple-choice items blank is not going to help you either.

  Now comes the exciting part. If you can rule out one of the four answer choices, your chances of answering correctly are now one out of three. You can almost see your MSP score improving right before your eyes.

  Although it is always better to be prepared for the test and to study in school, we all have to guess at one time or another. Some of us do not like to guess because we are afraid of choosing the wrong answer, but on the MSP, it is better to guess than leave an answer blank. Think about Jess.

There was a smart girl named Jess,
Who thought it was useless to guess.
If a question was tough,
She just gave up.
This only added to her stress.

- **Use a "code" to help you make good guesses on the MSP.**

  Some students use a "code" to rate each answer when they feel they might have to guess. Using your pencil in the test booklet, you can mark the following codes next to each multiple-choice response so you can make the best possible guess. The codes are as follows:

(+)   Putting a "plus sign" by your answer means you are not sure if this answer is correct, but you think this answer is probably more correct than the others.

(?)   Putting a "question mark" by your answer means you are unsure if this is the correct answer, but you don't want to rule it out completely.

(−)   Putting a "minus sign" by your answer means you are pretty sure this is the wrong answer. You should then choose from the other answers to make an educated guess.

Remember, it is fine to write in your test booklet. Think about Dwight.

There was a smart kid named Dwight,
Who marked answers that looked to be right.
He'd put a plus sign
Or a dash or a line.
Now the whole world knows he is bright!

- **Use what you know to "power guess."**

Not everything you know was learned in a classroom. Part of what you know comes from just living your life. When you take the MSP, you should use everything you have learned in school, but you should also use your experiences outside the classroom to help you answer questions correctly. Using your "common sense," as well as other information you know, will help you do especially well on the MSP. Try to use what you know from the world around you to eliminate obviously wrong answers. If you can rule out just one answer that you are certain is not correct, you are going to greatly increase your chances of guessing another answer correctly. For example, if you are given a question in which you are asked to find the square footage of a home, and one of the answers seems very small, you might be able to count that answer out using your own experiences. Although the mathematics might be difficult for you, your common sense has eliminated one likely wrong answer. Think about Drew.

There was a boy named Drew,
Who forgot to use what he knew.
He had lots of knowledge.
He could have been in college!
But his right answers were few.

• **Do Not Get Stuck on One Question.**

One of the worst things you can do on the MSP is to get stuck on one question. The MSP gives you many chances to show all that you have learned. Not knowing the answer to one or two questions is not going to hurt your test results very much.

When you become stuck on a question, your mind plays tricks on you. You begin to think that you are a total failure, and your worries become greater and greater. This worrying gets in the way of your doing well on the rest of the test. Remember, very few students know all the answers on the MSP. If you are not sure of the answer after spending some time on it, mark it in your test booklet and come back to it later. When you to come back to that question later, you might find a new way of thinking. Sometimes, another question or answer later in the test will remind you of a possible answer to the question that had seemed difficult. If not, you can use your guessing strategies to solve the questions you are unsure of after you have answered all the questions you know. Also, when you move on from a troubling question and find you are able to answer other questions correctly, you will feel much better about yourself and you will feel calmer. This will help you have a better chance of succeeding on a question that made you feel "stuck." Think about Von.

There was a sweet girl named Von,
Who got stuck and just couldn't go on.
She'd sit there and stare,
But the answer wasn't there.
Before she knew it, all the time was gone.

• **Always, and This Means Always, Recheck Your Work.**

Everyone makes mistakes. People make the most mistakes when they feel a little worried or rushed. Checking your work is a very important part of doing your best on the MSP. This is particularly true in the Mathematics section, where careless mistakes can lead to a wrong answer, even when the student used the right steps. Going back and rechecking your work is very important. You can read a paragraph over again if there is something you do not understand or something that you forgot. In the Mathematics section, look at your calculations to make sure that you did not mistake one number for another and that you lined up your calculations neatly and legibly. If any numbers seem messy or unreadable, you might want to recheck your calculations. If an answer does not seem to make sense, go back and reread the question, or recheck your work. Think about Jen.

There was a quick girl named Jen,
Who read stuff once and never again.
It would have been nice
If she'd reread it twice.
Her test scores would be better then!

- **Pay Attention to Yourself and Not Others.**

  It is easy to look around the room and wonder how friends are doing on the MSP. However, it is important to think about how you are using tools and strategies on the MSP. Don't become distracted by friends. You are going to waste a lot of time if you try to figure out what your friends are doing. Instead, use that time to "show what you know."

  If it becomes hard for you to pay attention, give yourself a little break. If you feel you are getting a little tense or worried, or if a question seems tough, close your eyes for a second or two. Think positive thoughts about the MSP. Try to put negative thoughts out of your mind. You might want to stretch your arms or feet or move around a little to help you focus. Anything you may do to help pay better attention to the test is a great test-taking strategy. Think about Kirk.

There was a boy named Kirk,
Who thought of everything but his work.
He stared into the air
And squirmed in his chair.
When his test scores come, he won't look!

Writing

Introduction

The Writing Assessment of the Measurements of Student Progress (MSP) will measure how well you communicate ideas in writing. The Writing Assessment is based on the writing skills you have been taught in school through seventh grade. It is not meant to confuse or trick you but to allow you to have the best chance to show what you know.

The *Show What You Know® on the MSP for Grade 7, Student Workbook* includes a Writing Practice Tutorial that will help you practice your test-taking skills. Following the Writing Practice Tutorial is a full-length Writing Assessment. Both the Writing Practice Tutorial and the Writing Assessment have been created to model the Grade 7 Measurements of Student Progress for Writing.

About the Writing MSP

The Grade 7 Writing Assessment consists of two writing tasks. Session One of the Writing Assessment is designed to elicit an expository response. An expository response is one that explains why or informs about something. The writer should present information in a way that enhances the reader's understanding of the topic. Session Two of the Writing MSP will focus on a persuasive response. A persuasive response is one that is primarily written to persuade or convince the designated audience to support a point of view, make a decision, or take an action.

Both of the writing tasks will allow you to follow all of the steps of the writing process: prewriting, writing a first draft, revising, editing, and writing a final draft. Both tasks have accompanying scoring criteria (checklists) which focus on qualities of good expository or persuasive writing. For each of these writing tasks, you are allowed to use a commercially published thesaurus and dictionary in print form. No electronic tools may be used. Scratch paper will be available for your prewriting and first draft activities.

Item Distribution on the MSP for Grade 7

	Writing Tasks	Possible Points: Conventions	Possible Points: Content, Style, Organization	Total Possible Points
	1 Expository	2	4	6
	1 Persuasive	2	4	6
Total Numbers	2 Tasks			12

Scoring

On the MSP for Grade 7 Writing Assessment, you will be tested on two writing tasks worth up to six points each. Each writing task will be scored using a 2-point rubric for conventions and a 4-point rubric for content, style, and organization. The total number of points from the two writing tasks will determine your Writing test score.

Grade 7
Conventions Scoring Guide

Points	Description
2	• Consistently follows the rules of Standard English for grammar and usage • Consistently follows the rules of Standard English for spelling of commonly used words • Consistently follows the rules of Standard English for capitalization • Consistently follows the rules of Standard English for punctuation • Exhibits the use of complete sentences except where purposeful fragments are used for effect • Indicates paragraphs consistently
1	• Generally follows the rules of Standard English for grammar and usage • Generally follows the rules of Standard English for spelling of commonly used words • Generally follows the rules of Standard English for capitalization • Generally follows the rules of Standard English for punctuation • Generally exhibits the use of complete sentences except where purposeful fragments are used for effect • Indicates paragraphs for the most part
0	• Mostly does not follow the rules of Standard English for grammar and usage • Mostly does not follow the rules of Standard English for spelling of commonly used words • Mostly does not follow the rules of Standard English for capitalization • Mostly does not follow the rules of Standard English for punctuation • Exhibits errors in sentence structure that impede communication • Mostly does not indicate paragraphs
Z	• Response is "I don't know"; response is a question mark (?); response is one word; response is only the title of the prompt; or the prompt is simply recopied

Principles of Holistic Scoring:

• **Density:** Weigh the proportion of errors to the amount of writing done well. This includes the ratio of errors to length.

• **Variety:** Consider the range of errors across the categories included in the rubric (usage, grammar, spelling, capitalization, punctuation, sentence formation, and paragraphing).

• **Severity:** Weigh basic errors more heavily than higher level errors. Also, weigh basic spelling and sentence formation errors more heavily.

Grade 7
Content, Organization, and Style Scoring Guide

Points	Description
4	• Maintains consistent focus on topic and has selected and relevant details • Has a logical organizational pattern and conveys a sense of wholeness and completeness • Provides transitions which clearly serve to connect ideas • Uses language effectively by exhibiting word choices that are engaging and appropriate for intended audience and purpose • Includes sentences, or phrases where appropriate, of varied length and structure • Allows the reader to sense the person behind the words
3	• Maintains adequate focus on the topic and has adequate supporting details • Has a logical organizational pattern and conveys a sense of wholeness and completeness, although some lapses occur • Provides adequate transitions in an attempt to connect ideas • Uses adequate language and appropriate word choices for intended audience and purpose • Includes sentences, or phrases where appropriate, that are somewhat varied in length and structure • Provides the reader with some sense of the person behind the words
2	• Demonstrates an inconsistent focus and includes some supporting details, but may include extraneous or loosely related material • Shows an attempt at an organizational pattern, but exhibits little sense of wholeness and completeness • Provides transitions which are weak or inconsistent • Has a limited and predictable vocabulary which may not be appropriate for the intended audience and purpose • Shows limited variety in sentence length and structure • Attempts somewhat to give the reader a sense of the person behind the words
1	• Demonstrates little or no focus and few supporting details which may be inconsistent or interfere with the meaning of the text • Has little evidence of an organizational pattern or any sense of wholeness and completeness • Provides transitions which are poorly utilized, or fails to provide transitions • Has a limited or inappropriate vocabulary for the intended audience and purpose • Has little or no variety in sentence length and structure • Provides the reader with little sense of the person behind the words
Z	• Response is "I don't know"; response is a question mark (?); response is one word; response is only the title of the prompt; or the prompt is simply recopied

Glossary

alliteration: Repeating the same sound at the beginning of several words in a phrase or sentence. For example, "The bees buzzed in the back of the blue barn."

analyze: To study something carefully.

audience: The readers of a written work.

author's purpose: The reason why an author is writing a text. For example, the author may be writing to persuade, to entertain, to describe, or to explain.

bias: A strong feeling for or against without reason; prejudice.

cluster: During prewriting, a writer will group together ideas for a writing piece. The ideas are organized by main idea and supporting details.

constructed response: A test question in the MSP that requires students to write a response.

context: The words that come before and after a particular word or phrase in a piece of writing. Context helps to explain its full meaning.

conventions: The rules of standard English usage, such as capitalization, punctuation, paragraphing, and spelling.

credibility: A piece of writing that is believable.

declarative sentence: A sentence that makes a statement and ends with a period.

descriptive: Using vivid and powerful words to create a clear picture of a person, place, thing, or idea.

details: To tell or describe things in writing.

draft: A stage in the writing process. The writing piece is not in its final form; it still needs to be revised and edited.

edit: In the writing process, to check the writing for correct spelling, punctuation, capitalization, usage, paragraph indentation, neatness, and legibility (able to read the author's writing). Editing usually occurs in the final part of the writing process.

essay: A short piece of writing that gives the author's opinion on a certain subject. Examples of an essay may be how to do something, comparison and contrast, or cause and effect.

exclamatory sentence: A sentence that shows strong feelings or excitement. It ends with an exclamation point (!).

expository writing: A piece of writing that explains an idea and informs the reader.

fiction: A made-up story. Fiction has a title, named characters, and events that detail what happens.

figurative language (also known as figures of speech): An expression in which words are used in an imaginative or colorful way. For example, the sentence, "It is raining cats and dogs!" is a figure of speech. Metaphors, personification, and similes are figures of speech.

flashback: An interruption in the present action of a story to flash backward and tell what happened at an earlier time.

focus: When the writer keeps his/her purpose clear all through his or her writing.

foreshadowing: Giving hints or clues of what might happen at a future time in the story.

free writing: A kind of prewriting in which the writer drafts quickly, without stopping, editing, or self-correcting, to see what he or she knows, thinks, or feels.

genre: Putting literary and informational works into categories (e.g., drama, essay, biography, mystery, poetry).

Glossary

imagery: Using words that help produce pictures in the mind.

imperative sentence: A sentence that gives a command or makes a request.

interpret: To read something and draw conclusions about an object, person, or event.

interrogative sentence: A sentence that asks a question and ends with a question mark (?).

main idea: The main reason a piece of writing was written. Usually, the main idea is found in the first sentence of each paragraph.

mode: A type of writing. Examples of modes of writing include narratives, retelling, journals, letters, directions, invitations, thank-you notes, summaries, informational reports, and persuasive letters.

mood: A feeling or emotion the reader gets from a piece of writing.

narrative writing: Writing about a series of events in a purposeful order (sequence) to tell a story; the writing can be fiction or factual. A narrative contains a plot, characters, setting, dialogue, chronological sequence, and theme.

nonfiction: Writing about real people, places, and things that are true.

noun: The name of a person, place, or thing.

onomatopoeia: The use of words in which the sounds of the word suggests the sound associated with it. For example, buzz, hiss, splat.

paragraph: A group of sentences that are about a main idea. You can tell when a new paragraph begins when the first word of the sentence is indented or if a line space is inserted between sections of writing.

paraphrase: To restate the ideas of a text in your own words.

persuasive writing: Writing that may change the thinking of a reader or may move the reader to action.

plan: Occurs in the early stages of writing when the writer pulls together ideas and a purpose for the written piece.

plot: A series of events that make up a story.

point of view: The way a story is told; it could be in first person, omniscient, or in third person.

prefix: A group of letters added to the beginning of a word. For example, untie, rebuild, preteen.

preposition: A word that links another word or group of words to other parts of the sentence. Examples are in, on, of, at, by, between, outside, etc.

prewriting: The thinking and planning the writer does before drafting. Prewriting includes considering the topic, audience, and purpose; gathering information; choosing a form (mode); determining the role of the writer; and making a plan.

prompt: A writing task. In the MSP, students will be instructed to write to a specific topic.

pronoun: A word that refers to a particular person, place, or thing.

proofreading: Editing a written work.

published work: The final writing draft shared with the audience.

reliable: Sources used for writing that are trustworthy.

revise: To rework your writing to improve it.

sentence: A group of words that express a complete thought. It has a subject and a verb.

Glossary

style: A way of writing that is individual to the writer, such as the writer's choice of words, phrases, and images.

suffix: A group of letters added to the end of a word. For example, teach<u>er</u>, color<u>ful</u>, sugar<u>less</u>, etc.

summary: To retell what happens in a story in a short way by telling the main ideas, not details.

theme: The central or main idea of a piece of writing.

tone: How the writer feels about a subject, such as happy, sad, hopeful, angry, helpful, etc.

topic sentence: A sentence that states the main idea of the paragraph.

transition: A word that links ideas together.

verb: A word that shows action or being.

voice: The opinion of the author that comes through in the writing.

word web: A graphic organizer created by the writer during prewriting. A web is used to gather and connect facts, ideas, concepts, and words.

This page intentionally left blank.

Writing Tutorial

The Writing Tutorial is made up of two writing prompts. These questions show you how the skills you have learned in Writing class may be tested on the Writing MSP. The questions also give you a chance to practice your skills. If you have trouble with a question, talk with a parent or teacher.

To respond to the writing prompt, use the prewriting page that follows the prompt to plan your composition and then write your final composition on the lined pages marked Final Draft.

Directions for the Writing Tutorial

Directions to the Student

Today you will begin the Writing Tutorial. This is an assessment of how well you communicate ideas in writing.

For this part of the assessment, you will have two writing tasks. You will do one of the writing tasks today and one on another day. **In order to earn the best possible score, be sure you follow directions and write in the assigned mode/purpose for each task**.

Both of these writing tasks will allow you to follow all of the steps of the writing process: prewriting, writing a first draft, revising, editing, and writing a final draft. Both tasks have accompanying scoring criteria.

There is space provided in the test booklet for prewriting. You will receive several pieces of scratch paper for your prewriting (if you need more space) and writing your first draft. However, you must write your final draft for each writing task in this booklet.

Please note: For each of the writing tasks, the only piece of writing that will be scored is what is written in this booklet. Additional pages inserted into this booklet will not be scored.

There are several important things to remember:

1. You will have as much time as you need for **each** writing task, but you must finish each task by the end of the day.

2. For each of these writing tasks you are allowed to use a commercially published thesaurus and dictionary in print form. No electronic tools may be used.

3. Your final draft for each writing task must be written in this booklet on the pages provided. Additional pages inserted in this booklet will not be scored.

4. You must write your final draft using a **No. 2 pencil**, not a mechanical pencil or pen. If you do not have a No. 2 pencil, ask your teacher to give you one.

5. When writing each of your final drafts in this booklet, be sure to write neatly and clearly on the lines provided. Cross out or erase any work you do not want to include as part of your final draft.

6. If you finish a writing task early, you may check over your work on that writing task only.

7. When you reach the word **STOP** in your booklet, do not go on until you are told to turn the page.

Go on ▶

Sample Question

To help you understand how to answer the test questions, look at the sample writing task below. This sample does not refer to the writing tasks you are about to read. It is included to show you what the writing tasks in the assessment are like and how to write your final draft.

End of Year Field Trip

> Your class is planning its end of the year field trip. Your teacher has asked each student to submit one idea of where the class should go. In a multi-paragraph letter, <u>persuade</u> your teacher to choose your field trip location.

Dear Mr. Long,

I believe our class field trip should be both educational and fun. Therefore, my suggestion for our class field trip is a visit to Olentangy Caverns.

A visit to Olentangy Caverns is educational in two ways. First, the caverns are full of several different kinds of rocks and gems. Studying the different types of rocks would be a way to study science. Second, the caverns are very old and full of Native American artifacts. Studying the artifacts would be an interesting way to study history.

Go on ▶

Taking a trip to Olentangy Caverns would be fun too. There are lots of caves to explore. Climbing through the caves is very exciting and sometimes even a little scary.

Another fun activity at Olentangy Caverns is mining for gems. Sifting through the rocks and dirt, you can discover semi-precious gemstones that you are allowed to keep.

Olentangy Caverns would be the best choice for our class field trip because it would be a fun and educational place to visit. I think everyone in our class would enjoy a field trip to Olentangy Caverns.

Sincerely,

Fred

Go on ▶

                   © Englefield & Associates, Inc.

Grade 7
Checklist for Writing to Explain

My essay or letter will explain successfully if I include thoughtful and specific content and organize my writing well. That means I should

- ❏ follow the directions given in the writing prompt;
- ❏ narrow my topic;
- ❏ stay focused on the main ideas;
- ❏ elaborate by using reasons, well-chosen and specific details, examples, and/or anecdotes to support my ideas;
- ❏ include information that is interesting, thoughtful, and necessary for my audience to know;
- ❏ organize my writing with an introduction, supporting paragraphs with main points and elaboration, and an effective conclusion;
- ❏ organize my writing in paragraphs;
- ❏ use transitions to connect my ideas.

My essay or letter will explain successfully if I demonstrate an effective style. That means I should

- ❏ show that I care about my topic by writing in a voice appropriate for my audience and purpose,
- ❏ use language that is appropriate for my audience and purpose,
- ❏ use specific words and phrases that help the reader understand my ideas,
- ❏ use different types and lengths of sentences.

My essay or letter will be more effective if I follow conventions in writing. That means I should

- ❏ follow the rules of grammar and Standard English usage,
- ❏ spell words correctly,
- ❏ use correct capitalization,
- ❏ use correct punctuation,
- ❏ write complete sentences,
- ❏ show where new paragraphs begin.

Go on ▶

Expository Writing Task

Directions: Today you will write an expository letter. (For security reasons, please do not include your personal return address in your letter.)

In expository writing, a writer fully explains the main idea or thesis using details, reasons, and/or examples. In order to earn the best possible score, be sure you follow directions and write in the expository mode.

For this writing task, you will have the opportunity to follow all of the steps of the writing process: prewriting, writing a first draft, revising, editing, and writing a final draft. You may use a commercially published thesaurus and dictionary in print form. No electronic tools may be used.

The only piece of writing that will be scored is your final draft in this test booklet. Your score will be based on the scoring criteria listed on the previous page. Be sure to look at this checklist of scoring criteria to help you write an effective expository letter. Additional pages inserted into this booklet will not be scored.

Attending a Drama Club Production

> Last weekend you attended the Drama Club's production of *Romeo and Juliet*.
> Compose a letter to the editor of your school paper <u>explaining</u> why you enjoyed
> the performance.

Go on ▶

Expository Writing Task

Prewriting

Directions: Prewriting is a great way to get started on a writing task because it gives you ideas to start with. It also helps you organize your ideas before you write. There are different kinds of prewriting. Choose **one** of the following, or another one that you know and like, and use the next page (and additional scratch paper if you need more space) to do the prewriting.

- Draw a **web** or **cluster** with circles connected by lines. In the circles, write ideas that develop and support your topic (details, reasons, and/or examples). Draw lines to connect ideas that are related in some way. Then, decide how you will organize your ideas.

OR

- **List** ideas that develop and support your topic. You don't have to write complete sentences. At first, don't worry about the order of the ideas. After you have finished your list, go back and organize your ideas.

OR

- Do an **outline**.

OR

- Do **another kind of prewriting** that you know and like.

Go on ▶

Prewriting

After you finish your prewriting, use the scrap paper your teacher gave you for your first draft.

Go on ▶

Final Draft

Directions: Before you begin your final draft, read the checklist again. Then make revisions and edits to your first draft according to the checklist. When you have made your revisions and edits, write your final draft on this page and the next four pages if you need them.

After you have finished writing your final draft in the booklet, read the checklist one more time to make sure you have done your best writing. If you need to do any final editing, do it on your final draft. You may use a commercially published thesaurus and dictionary in print form to help with your words. **Spell check may not be used.** Your final draft **will be scored**.

Attending a Drama Club Production

> Last weekend you attended the Drama Club's production of *Romeo and Juliet*. Compose a letter to the editor of your school paper <u>explaining</u> why you enjoyed the performance.

_____

_____

_____

_____

_____

_____

_____

_____

_____

Go on ▶

You may continue your final draft on this page.

_____

_____

_____

_____

_____

_____

_____

_____

_____

_____

_____

_____

_____

_____

_____

_____

_____

_____

_____

Go on ▶

You may continue your final draft on this page.

_____

_____

_____

_____

_____

_____

_____

_____

_____

_____

_____

_____

_____

_____

_____

_____

_____

_____

_____

Go on ▶

You may continue your final draft on this page.

_____

_____

_____

_____

_____

_____

_____

_____

_____

_____

_____

_____

_____

_____

_____

_____

_____

Go on ▶

You may continue your final draft on this page.

_____

_____

_____

_____

_____

_____

_____

_____

_____

_____

_____

_____

_____

_____

_____

_____

_____

_____

STOP

Scoring Criteria for Persuasive Writing

Grade 7
Checklist for Writing to Persuade

My essay or letter will be persuasive if I include thoughtful and specific content and organize my writing well. That means I should

- ❏ follow the directions given in the writing prompt;
- ❏ have a clear position and stay focused on that position;
- ❏ have more than one argument to support my position;
- ❏ elaborate by using reasons, well-chosen and specific details, examples, anecdotes, facts, and/or statistics as evidence to support my arguments;
- ❏ organize my writing to make the best case for my position;
- ❏ consider the opposing argument(s) and, if important, refute (prove false);
- ❏ begin my writing with an opening, include a statement of position, and end my writing with an effective persuasive conclusion, such as a call for action;
- ❏ use transitions to connect my position, arguments, and evidence.

My essay or letter will be persuasive if I demonstrate an interesting style. That means I should

- ❏ show that I am committed to my position by writing in a voice appropriate for my audience and purpose;
- ❏ use words, phrases, and persuasive techniques that urge or compel the reader to support my position;
- ❏ use different types and lengths of sentences.

My essay or letter will be more effective if I follow conventions in writing. That means I should

- ❏ follow the rules of grammar and Standard English usage,
- ❏ spell words correctly,
- ❏ use correct capitalization,
- ❏ use correct punctuation,
- ❏ write complete sentences,
- ❏ show where new paragraphs begin.

Go on ▶

Persuasive Writing Task

Directions: Today you will write a persuasive letter. (For security reasons, please do not include your personal return address in your letter.)

In persuasive writing, the writer tries to convince an audience to support his or her position using reasons, examples, and/or evidence. In order to receive the best possible score, be sure you follow directions and write in the persuasive mode.

For this writing task, you will have the opportunity to follow all of the steps of the writing process: prewriting, writing a first draft, revising, editing, and writing a final draft. You may use a commercially published thesaurus and dictionary in print form. No electronic tools may be used.

The only piece of writing that will be scored is your final draft in this test booklet. Your score will be based on the scoring criteria listed on the previous page. Be sure to refer to this checklist of scoring criteria to help you write an effective persuasive letter. Additional pages inserted into this booklet will not be scored.

Walking to Nearby Restaurants

> **Your principal is considering allowing students to walk to nearby restaurants for lunch. In a multi-paragraph letter, <u>persuade</u> your principal to allow students to leave school grounds during their lunch period.**

Go on ▶

Persuasive Writing Task

Prewriting

Directions: Prewriting is a great way to get started on a writing task because it gives you ideas to start with. It also helps you organize your ideas before you write. There are different kinds of prewriting. Choose **one** of the following, or another one that you know and like, and use the next page (and additional scratch paper if you need more space) to do the prewriting.

- Draw a **web or cluster** with circles connected by lines. In the circles, write ideas for supporting your position (reasons, examples, and/or evidence). Draw lines to connect ideas that are related in some way. Then, decide how you will organize your ideas.

OR

- **List** ideas that support your position. You don't have to write complete sentences. At first, don't worry about the order of the ideas. After you have finished your list, go back and organize your ideas.

OR

- Do an **outline**.

OR

- Do **another kind of prewriting** that you know and like.

Go on ▶

Prewriting

After you finish your prewriting, use the scrap paper your teacher gave you for your first draft.

Go on ▸

Final Draft

Directions: Before you begin your final draft, read the checklist again. Then make revisions and edits to your first draft according to the checklist. When you have made your revisions and edits, write your final draft on this page and the next four pages if you need them.

After you have finished writing your final draft in the booklet, read the checklist one more time to make sure you have done your best writing. If you need to do any final editing, do it on your final draft. You may use a commercially published thesaurus and dictionary in print form to help with your words. **Spell check may not be used.** Your final draft **will be scored**.

Walking to Nearby Restaurants

> **Your principal is considering allowing students to walk to nearby restaurants for lunch. In a multi-paragraph letter, <u>persuade</u> your principal to allow students to leave school grounds during their lunch period.**

_____

_____

_____

_____

_____

_____

_____

_____

_____

Go on ▶

You may continue your final draft on this page.

_____

_____

_____

_____

_____

_____

_____

_____

_____

_____

_____

_____

_____

_____

_____

_____

Go on ▶

You may continue your final draft on this page.

_____

_____

_____

_____

_____

_____

_____

_____

_____

_____

_____

_____

_____

_____

_____

_____

_____

Go on ▶

You may continue your final draft on this page.

_____

_____

_____

_____

_____

_____

_____

_____

_____

_____

_____

_____

_____

_____

_____

_____

_____

Go on ▶

You may continue your final draft on this page.

_____

_____

_____

_____

_____

_____

_____

_____

_____

_____

_____

_____

_____

_____

_____

_____

_____

_____

STOP

Writing Assessment

The Writing Assessment is made up of two writing prompts. These questions show you how the skills you have learned in Writing class may be tested on the Writing MSP. The questions also give you a chance to practice your skills. If you have trouble with a question, talk with a parent or teacher.

To respond to the writing prompt, use the prewriting page that follows the prompt to plan your composition and then write your final composition on the lined pages marked Final Draft.

Directions for the Writing Assessment

Directions to the Student

Today you will begin the Writing Assessment. This is an assessment of how well you communicate ideas in writing.

For this part of the assessment, you will have two writing tasks. You will do one of the writing tasks today and one on another day. **In order to earn the best possible score, be sure you follow directions and write in the assigned mode/purpose for each task**.

Both of these writing tasks will allow you to follow all of the steps of the writing process: prewriting, writing a first draft, revising, editing, and writing a final draft. Both tasks have accompanying scoring criteria.

There is space provided in the test booklet for prewriting. You will receive several pieces of scratch paper for your prewriting (if you need more space) and writing your first draft. However, you must write your final draft for each writing task in this booklet.

Please note: For each of the writing tasks, the only piece of writing that will be scored is what is written in this booklet. Additional pages inserted into this booklet will not be scored.

There are several important things to remember:

1. You will have as much time as you need for **each** writing task, but you must finish each task by the end of the day.

2. For each of these writing tasks you are allowed to use a commercially published thesaurus and dictionary in print form. No electronic tools may be used.

3. Your final draft for each writing task must be written in this booklet on the pages provided. Additional pages inserted in this booklet will not be scored.

4. You must write your final draft using a **No. 2 pencil**, not a mechanical pencil or pen. If you do not have a No. 2 pencil, ask your teacher to give you one.

5. When writing each of your final drafts in this booklet, be sure to write neatly and clearly on the lines provided. Cross out or erase any work you do not want to include as part of your final draft.

6. If you finish a writing task early, you may check over your work on that writing task only.

7. When you reach the word **STOP** in your booklet, do not go on until you are told to turn the page.

Go on ▶

Scoring Criteria for Expository Writing

Grade 7
Checklist for Writing to Explain

My essay or letter will explain successfully if I include thoughtful and specific content and organize my writing well. That means I should

- ❑ follow the directions given in the writing prompt;
- ❑ narrow my topic;
- ❑ stay focused on the main ideas;
- ❑ elaborate by using reasons, well-chosen and specific details, examples, and/or anecdotes to support my ideas;
- ❑ include information that is interesting, thoughtful, and necessary for my audience to know;
- ❑ organize my writing with an introduction, supporting paragraphs with main points and elaboration, and an effective conclusion;
- ❑ organize my writing in paragraphs;
- ❑ use transitions to connect my ideas.

My essay or letter will explain successfully if I demonstrate an effective style. That means I should

- ❑ show that I care about my topic by writing in a voice appropriate for my audience and purpose,
- ❑ use language that is appropriate for my audience and purpose,
- ❑ use specific words and phrases that help the reader understand my ideas,
- ❑ use different types and lengths of sentences.

My essay or letter will be more effective if I follow conventions in writing. That means I should

- ❑ follow the rules of grammar and Standard English usage,
- ❑ spell words correctly,
- ❑ use correct capitalization,
- ❑ use correct punctuation,
- ❑ write complete sentences,
- ❑ show where new paragraphs begin.

Go on ▶

Expository Writing Task

Directions: Today you will write an expository letter. (For security reasons, please do not include your personal return address in your letter.)

In expository writing, a writer fully explains the main idea or thesis using details, reasons, and/or examples. In order to earn the best possible score, be sure you follow directions and write in the expository mode.

For this writing task, you will have the opportunity to follow all of the steps of the writing process: prewriting, writing a first draft, revising, editing, and writing a final draft. You may use a commercially published thesaurus and dictionary in print form. No electronic tools may be used.

The only piece of writing that will be scored is your final draft in this test booklet. Your score will be based on the scoring criteria listed on the previous page. Be sure to look at this checklist of scoring criteria to help you write an effective expository letter. Additional pages inserted into this booklet will not be scored.

Last Movie

> **What was the last movie you watched? Compose a multi-paragraph letter to your friend <u>explaining</u> why you enjoyed the movie.**

Go on ▶

Expository Writing Task

Prewriting

Directions: Prewriting is a great way to get started on a writing task because it gives you ideas to start with. It also helps you organize your ideas before you write. There are different kinds of prewriting. Choose **one** of the following, or another one that you know and like, and use the next page (and additional scratch paper if you need more space) to do the prewriting.

- Draw a **web** or **cluster** with circles connected by lines. In the circles, write ideas that develop and support your topic (details, reasons, and/or examples). Draw lines to connect ideas that are related in some way. Then, decide how you will organize your ideas.

OR

- **List** ideas that develop and support your topic. You don't have to write complete sentences. At first, don't worry about the order of the ideas. After you have finished your list, go back and organize your ideas.

OR

- Do an **outline**.

OR

- Do **another kind of prewriting** that you know and like.

Go on ▶

Prewriting

After you finish your prewriting, use the scrap paper your teacher gave you for your first draft.

Go on ▶

Final Draft

Directions: Before you begin your final draft, read the checklist again. Then make revisions and edits to your first draft according to the checklist. When you have made your revisions and edits, write your final draft on this page and the next four pages if you need them.

After you have finished writing your final draft in the booklet, read the checklist one more time to make sure you have done your best writing. If you need to do any final editing, do it on your final draft. You may use a commercially published thesaurus and dictionary in print form to help with your words. **Spell check may not be used.** Your final draft **will be scored**.

Last Movie

> **What was the last movie you watched? Compose a multi-paragraph letter to your friend <u>explaining</u> why you enjoyed the movie.**

_____

_____

_____

_____

_____

_____

_____

_____

Go on ▶

You may continue your final draft on this page.

_____

_____

_____

_____

_____

_____

_____

_____

_____

_____

_____

_____

_____

_____

_____

_____

_____

_____

Go on ▶

You may continue your final draft on this page.

_____

_____

_____

_____

_____

_____

_____

_____

_____

_____

_____

_____

_____

_____

_____

_____

_____

Go on ▶

You may continue your final draft on this page.

_____

_____

_____

_____

_____

_____

_____

_____

_____

_____

_____

_____

_____

_____

_____

_____

_____

_____

_____

Go on ▶

Copying is Prohibited © **Englefield & Associates, Inc.**

You may continue your final draft on this page.

_____

_____

_____

_____

_____

_____

_____

_____

_____

_____

_____

_____

_____

_____

_____

_____

_____

STOP

Scoring Criteria for Persuasive Writing

Grade 7
Checklist for Writing to Persuade

My essay or letter will be persuasive if I include thoughtful and specific content and organize my writing well. That means I should

- ❑ follow the directions given in the writing prompt;
- ❑ have a clear position and stay focused on that position;
- ❑ have more than one argument to support my position;
- ❑ elaborate by using reasons, well-chosen and specific details, examples, anecdotes, facts, and/or statistics as evidence to support my arguments;
- ❑ organize my writing to make the best case for my position;
- ❑ consider the opposing argument(s) and, if important, refute (prove false);
- ❑ begin my writing with an opening, include a statement of position, and end my writing with an effective persuasive conclusion, such as a call for action;
- ❑ use transitions to connect my position, arguments, and evidence.

My essay or letter will be persuasive if I demonstrate an interesting style. That means I should

- ❑ show that I am committed to my position by writing in a voice appropriate for my audience and purpose;
- ❑ use words, phrases, and persuasive techniques that urge or compel the reader to support my position;
- ❑ use different types and lengths of sentences.

My essay or letter will be more effective if I follow conventions in writing. That means I should

- ❑ follow the rules of grammar and Standard English usage,
- ❑ spell words correctly,
- ❑ use correct capitalization,
- ❑ use correct punctuation,
- ❑ write complete sentences,
- ❑ show where new paragraphs begin.

Go on ▶

Persuasive Writing Task

Directions: Today you will write a persuasive letter. (For security reasons, please do not include your personal return address in your letter.)

In persuasive writing, the writer tries to convince an audience to support his or her position using reasons, examples, and/or evidence. In order to receive the best possible score, be sure you follow directions and write in the persuasive mode.

For this writing task, you will have the opportunity to follow all of the steps of the writing process: prewriting, writing a first draft, revising, editing, and writing a final draft. You may use a commercially published thesaurus and dictionary in print form. No electronic tools may be used.

The only piece of writing that will be scored is your final draft in this test booklet. Your score will be based on the scoring criteria listed on the previous page. Be sure to refer to this checklist of scoring criteria to help you write an effective persuasive letter. Additional pages inserted into this booklet will not be scored.

A Student Representative

> **Your teacher is looking for a student representative to help manage a charity fundraiser. In a multi-paragraph letter, <u>convince</u> your teacher that you would be the best student for the job.**

Go on ▶

Persuasive Writing Task

Prewriting

Directions: Prewriting is a great way to get started on a writing task because it gives you ideas to start with. It also helps you organize your ideas before you write. There are different kinds of prewriting. Choose **one** of the following, or another one that you know and like, and use the next page (and additional scratch paper if you need more space) to do the prewriting.

- Draw a **web or cluster** with circles connected by lines. In the circles, write ideas for supporting your position (reasons, examples, and/or evidence). Draw lines to connect ideas that are related in some way. Then, decide how you will organize your ideas.

OR

- **List** ideas that support your position. You don't have to write complete sentences. At first, don't worry about the order of the ideas. After you have finished your list, go back and organize your ideas.

OR

- Do an **outline**.

OR

- Do **another kind of prewriting** that you know and like.

Go on ▶

Prewriting

After you finish your prewriting, use the scrap paper your teacher gave you for your first draft.

Go on ▶

Final Draft

Directions: Before you begin your final draft, read the checklist again. Then make revisions and edits to your first draft according to the checklist. When you have made your revisions and edits, write your final draft on this page and the next four pages if you need them.

After you have finished writing your final draft in the booklet, read the checklist one more time to make sure you have done your best writing. If you need to do any final editing, do it on your final draft. You may use a commercially published thesaurus and dictionary in print form to help with your words. **Spell check may not be used.** Your final draft **will be scored.**

A Student Representative

> **Your teacher is looking for a student representative to help manage a charity fundraiser. In a multi-paragraph letter, <u>convince</u> your teacher that you would be the best student for the job.**

_____

_____

_____

_____

_____

_____

_____

_____

Go on ▶

You may continue your final draft on this page.

_____

_____

_____

_____

_____

_____

_____

_____

_____

_____

_____

_____

_____

_____

_____

_____

_____

_____

Go on ▶

You may continue your final draft on this page.

_____

_____

_____

_____

_____

_____

_____

_____

_____

_____

_____

_____

_____

_____

_____

_____

_____

Go on ➤

You may continue your final draft on this page.

_____

_____

_____

_____

_____

_____

_____

_____

_____

_____

_____

_____

_____

_____

_____

_____

_____

Go on ▶

You may continue your final draft on this page.

_____

_____

_____

_____

_____

_____

_____

_____

_____

_____

_____

_____

_____

_____

_____

_____

_____

_____

STOP

Reading

Introduction

The Reading Assessment of the Measurements of Student Progress (MSP) will measure how well you understand what you read. The Reading Assessment is based on the reading skills you have been taught in school through seventh grade. It is not meant to confuse or trick you but to allow you to have the best chance to show what you know.

The *Show What You Know® on the MSP for Grade 7, Student Workbook* includes a Reading Practice Tutorial that will help you practice your test-taking skills. Following the Reading Practice Tutorial, there are two full-length Reading Assessments. Both the Reading Practice Tutorial and the Reading Assessments have been created to model the Grade 7 Measurements of Student Progress for Reading.

About the Reading MSP

The Grade 7 Reading Assessment consists of six reading selections: two literary passages, two informational passages, and one paired passage, which could consist of informational/informational, informational/literary, or literary/literary. The Reading Assessment is given in one session.

For the Reading Assessment, you will read stories and other passages and answer some questions. There are two different types of questions. There are multiple-choice and short-answer questions. You may look back at the story or selction when you are answering the questions. However, you may not use resource materials during the Reading Assessment.

Item Distribution on the MSP for Grade 7 Reading

Text Types/ Strands	Number of Multiple Choice	Number of Short Answer
Literary Comprehension Analysis	15	2–4
Informational Comprehension Analysis	15	2–4
Total	30	5

Source: OSPI August 2009 information for Spring 2010 MSP

Scoring

On the MSP for Grade 7 Reading Assessment, each multiple-choice item is worth one point. Short-answer items will be scored on a scale of zero to two points. Responses are scored with emphasis on communication of ideas. Conventions of writing (sentence structure, word choice, usage, grammar, and mechanics) are generally disregarded unless they substantially interfere with communications.

Item and Point Totals

Type	Number of Items	Total Possible Points
Multiple Choice	30	30
Short Answer	5	10
Total	35	40

Scoring Rules for Short-Answer Items

Scoring rules for items that assess <u>main ideas and details</u>:
A **2-point** response shows thorough comprehension of the main idea and important details. It uses ample, relevant information from text(s) to support responses.

A **1-point** response shows partial comprehension of the main idea and important details (may grasp main idea but show difficulty distinguishing between important and unimportant details; may miss part of fundamental who/what/where/when/why). It attempts to use information from text(s) to support responses; support may be limited or irrelevant.

A **0-point** response shows little or no understanding of the passage main ideas and details.

Scoring rules for items that assess <u>analysis, interpretation, and critical thinking about text</u>:
A **2-point** response analyzes appropriate information and/or makes thoughtful connections between whole texts/parts of texts. It develops thoughtful interpretations of text. It uses sufficient, relevant evidence from text(s) to support claims.

A **1-point** response analyzes limited information and/or makes superficial connections between whole texts/parts of texts. It develops conventional or simplistic interpretations of text. It attempts to use evidence from text(s) to support claims; support may be limited or irrelevant.

A **0-point** response shows little or no understanding of the passage main ideas and details.

Scoring rules for items that assess <u>summarizing and paraphrasing main ideas</u>:
A **2-point** response shows thorough comprehension of main ideas.

A **1-point** response shows partial comprehension of main ideas.

A **0-point** response shows little or no understanding of the passage main ideas and details.

Glossary

affixes: Groups of syllables (i.e. prefixes, such as *anti–* or *post–*, and suffixes, such as *–ly* or *–ment*) which, when added to a word or a root, alters the meaning of the word.

alliteration: The repetition of the same sound, usually of a consonant, at the beginning of two or more words of a sentence or line of poetry (e.g., "Andrew Alligator always eats alphabet soup").

alliterative sentences: Repeating the same initial sound in two or more words of a sentence or line of poetry (e.g., Whitman's line, "all summer in the sound of the sea").

analogy: A comparison of two pairs that have the same relationship. The key is to discover the relationship between the first pair, so you can choose the correct second pair (e.g., part-to-whole, opposites).

analysis: Separation of a whole into its parts for individual study.

analyze: To compare in order to rank items by importance or to provide reasons. Identify the important parts that make up the whole and determine how the parts are related to one another.

anticipation guide: A flexible strategy used to activate students' thoughts and opinions about a topic and to link their prior knowledge to new material. For example, a series of teacher-generated statements about a topic that students respond to and discuss before reading.

antonyms: Words that mean the opposite (e.g., *light* is an antonym of *dark*).

assumptions: Statements or thoughts taken to be true without proof.

author's craft: Stylistic choices the author makes regarding such components as plot, characterization, structure, scenes, and dialogue to produce a desired effect.

author's perspective: The author's subjective view as reflected in his/her written expression.

author's purpose: The reason an author writes, such as to entertain, inform, or persuade.

author's style: The author's attitude as reflected in the format of the author's written expression.

author's tone: The author's attitude as reflected in the word choice of the author's written expression.

automaticity: Ability to recognize a word (or series of words) in text effortlessly and rapidly.

blend: In decoding, it is the reader's act of sounding out and then combining the sounds in a word to assist in the pronunciation.

common consonant sounds: Speech sounds made by obstructing air flow, causing audible friction in varying amounts. Common consonant sounds include: /b/, /k/, /d/, /f/, /g/, /h/, /j/, /l/, /m/, /n/, /p/, /kw/, /r/, /s/, /t/, /v/, /w/, /ks/, /y/, /z/.

common inflectional ending: A common suffix that changes the form or function of a word, but not its basic meaning, such as "–ed" in "sprayed," "–ing" in "gathering."

common sight words: Words that are immediately recognized as a whole and do not require word analysis for identification. These words usually have irregular spellings.

common vowel patterns: A vowel is the open sound. The mouth must be open to produce the sound of a vowel in a syllable. The most common vowel patterns are the sound/spellings that students encounter most frequently in text (e.g., ea, ee, oi, ow, ou, oo).

comprehension-monitoring strategies: Strategies used to monitor one's reading by being aware of what one does understand and what one does not understand. The reader's awareness determines which comprehension-repair strategies to apply.

comprehension-repair strategies: Strategies used by a reader to regain comprehension as a result of comprehension monitoring. These strategies include but are not limited to: re-reading, word recognition strategies, looking back, reading ahead, slowing down, paraphrasing by sections, using context, and taking notes. (Also referred to as "fix-up strategies.")

Glossary

comprehension strategies: A procedure or set of steps to follow in order to enhance text understanding (e.g., making inferences, predicting outcomes).

concepts of print: Insights about the ways in which print works. Basic concepts about print include: identification of a book's front and back covers and title page; directionality (knowledge that readers and writers move from left to right, top to bottom, front to back); spacing (distance used to separate words); recognition of letters and words; connection between spoken and written language; understanding of the function of capitalization and punctuation; sequencing and locating skills.

content area vocabulary: Vocabulary found in specific subject areas (e.g., "integer" in math and "pioneer" in social studies).

content/academic text: Text from literature, science, social studies, math, and other academic areas that students need to read to be academically successful in school.

content/academic vocabulary: Terms from literature, science, social studies, math, and other academic areas that students need to understand in order to be successful readers.

context: The social or cultural situation in which the spoken or written word occurs; also often used to refer to the material surrounding an unknown word.

context clues: Information from the surrounding text that helps identify a word or word group. Clues could be words, phrases, sentences, illustrations, syntax, typographic signals, definitions, examples, or restatements.

culturally relevant: Reading materials with which students in a classroom can identify or relate. Depending on the student cultural make-up in a classroom, relevant reading material can change from year to year.

decodable text: Reading materials that provide an intermediate step between words in isolation and authentic literature. Such texts are designed to give students an opportunity to learn to use their understanding of phonics in the course of reading connected text. Although decodable texts may contain sight words that have been previously taught, most words are wholly decodable on the basis of the letter-sound and spelling-sound correspondences taught and practiced in phonics lessons.

directionality: Understanding that materials printed in English progress from left to right and top to bottom.

electronic sources: Resources for gathering information such as the Internet, television, radio, CD-ROM encyclopedia, and so on.

elements of style: Word choice, voice, sentence structure, and sentence length.

environmental print: Any print found in the physical environment, such as street signs, billboards, labels, and business signs.

figurative language: Word images and figures of speech used to enrich language (e.g., simile, metaphor, personification).

fluency: Ability to read a text quickly with accuracy and expression; freedom from word-identification problems that might hinder comprehension in silent reading or the expression of ideas in oral reading; automaticity.

foreshadowing: A literary technique of giving clues about an event before it happens.

functional document: A technical document such as a business letter, computer manual, or trade publication that assists one in getting information in order to perform a task.

generalize: Taking what is known and using it to make an inference about the nature of similar text. Generalizations lead to transferable understandings that can be supported by fact. They describe the characteristics of classes or categories of persons, places, living and non-living things, and events.

Glossary

genres: Terms used to classify literary and informational works into categories (e.g., biography, mystery, historical fiction).

gist: The most central thought or idea in a text.

graphic features: Features that illustrate information in text such as graphs, charts, maps, diagrams, tables, etc.

graphic organizers: Organizers that provide a visual representation of facts and concepts from a text and their relationships within an organized frame. Valuable instructional tools used to show the order and completeness of a student's thought process graphically.

icons: Symbols on a computer screen that represent a certain function, command, or program on the computer's hard drive. When an icon is clicked on, some action is performed, such as opening or moving a file, making computing more user-friendly.

idiom: A word used in a special way that may be different from the literal meaning (e.g., "you drive me crazy" or "hit the deck").

independent level: The level at which the student reads fluently with excellent comprehension. The student demonstrates 95–100% comprehension of text.

infer: To understand something not directly stated in the text by using past experience and knowledge combined with the text.

inference: The reasoning involved in drawing a conclusion or making a logical judgment on the basis of indirect evidence and prior conclusions rather than direct evidence from the text.

inferred: Reached a specific conclusion using past experiences and knowledge combined with text evidence.

inflectional ending: A letter or group of letters which when added to the end of a word does not change its part of speech, but adjusts the word to fit the meaning of the sentence (e.g., girl, girls, jump, jumped, big, bigger).

informational/expository text: A form of written composition that has as its primary purpose explanation or the communication of details, facts, and discipline- or content-specific information (e.g., content area textbooks, encyclopedias, biographies).

instructional level: The level at which the student can make maximum progress in reading with teacher guidance. The student demonstrates 90–94% comprehension of text.

irony: The use of words to convey the opposite of their literal meaning: the words say one thing, but mean another. Often meant to reflect the author's tone or the attitude of a character or situation.

key word searches: A key term or phrase the computer uses in order to begin an online search for specific information.

language registry: The systematic differences of language use determined by regional, social or situational changes (e.g., a child might say "yup" at home, but would be expected to say "yes" at school).

letter patterns: Common letter groupings that represent specific sounds (e.g., *–ing* in "string" and *–ough* in "enough").

literary devices: Techniques used to convey or enhance an author's message or voice (e.g., idiom, figurative language, metaphor, exaggeration, dialogue, and imagery).

literary/narrative genres: Subcategories used to classify literary works, usually by form, technique, or content (e.g., novel, essay, short story, comedy, epic).

literary/narrative text: Text that describes action or events; usually includes a problem and resolution; usually, but not always, fiction.

Glossary

main idea: The gist of a passage; central thought; the chief topic of a passage which can be expressed or implied in a word or phrase; the topic sentence of a paragraph; a statement in sentence form which gives the stated or implied major topic of a passage and the specific way in which the passage is limited in content or reference.

mental imagery: Words or phrases that appeal to one or more of the five senses, allowing the reader to form mental pictures or images while reading.

metaphor: A figure of speech that compares two things without using the words *like* or *as* (e.g., laughter is the best medicine).

mood: The emotional state of mind expressed by an author or artist in his/her work, or the emotional atmosphere produced by an artistic work.

multiple-meaning words: Words with the same spelling and/or pronunciation which have more than one meaning depending on their context, such as "The wind blew" and "Please wind the clock."

non-technical documents: In this context, non-technical refers to documents (e.g., memos, lists, job applications) in which the content and vocabulary are not tied to a specific subject.

oddity tasks: In phonemic awareness, identifying which word in a set of three or four has the "odd" sound (e.g., run, rug, and toy).

onomatopoeia: A term used to describe words whose pronunciations suggest their meaning (e.g., meow, buzz). Words used to represent a sound.

onset and rime: Parts of spoken language that are syllables. An onset is the initial consonant(s) sound of a syllable (the onset of bag is *b*–; of swim, *sw*–). A rime is the part of the syllable that contains the vowel and all that follows it (the rime of bag is *–ag*; of swim, *–im*). Not all syllables or words have an onset, but they all have a rime (e.g., the word or syllable "out" is a rime without an onset).

oral language structure: Spoken language has five linguistic systems. They include the phonological (sounds of language), the syntactic (order and grammar), the semantic (meanings), the pragmatic (social interactive), and lexicon (vocabulary).

organizational features: Tools the author uses to organize ideas (e.g., caption and headings).

organizational structures: The organization of a text.

personification: A figure of speech in which nonhuman objects, such as ideas, objects, or animals, are given human characteristics (e.g., "flowers danced about the lawn").

persuasive devices: A technique the author uses to move the reader to his/her point of view, such as bias, overgeneralization, and association.

phoneme: The smallest unit of sound in a spoken word that makes a difference in the word's meaning.

phonemic awareness: The ability to hear, identify, and manipulate individual sounds (phonemes) in spoken words.

phonics: The understanding that there is a predictable relationship between phonemes (the sounds of spoken language) and graphemes (the letters and spellings that represent those sounds in written language).

phonological awareness: A general understanding of the sound structure of words, including rhymes, syllables, and phonemes.

plot: The structure of the events in a story, usually including rising action, climax, and resolution.

point of view: The perspective from which a story is told. The three points of view are first person, third person, and omniscient.

predict: To foresee what might happen in a text based on textual clues and a reader's background knowledge or schema.

predictions: Foretelling what might happen next in a story or poem by using textual clues and a reader's background knowledge or schema.

Glossary

prefix: An affix attached before a base word or root, such as re- in reprint. A prefix slightly alters the meaning of a root word. For example, reprint means to print again.

primary sources: The original source of resource information (e.g., letter, encyclopedia, book).

print conventions: The rules that govern the customary use of print in reading and writing including directionality of print, punctuation, and capitalization.

prior knowledge: The knowledge that stems from previous experience. Note: prior knowledge is a key component of the schema theory of reading comprehension.

propaganda: Written or oral presentations intended to persuade the audience to a particular point of view often by misrepresenting data or exaggerating the facts.

propaganda techniques: Methods used in creating propaganda, such as bandwagon, peer pressure, repetition, and testimonials/endorsements.

pull-down menu: A computer term that refers to a list of words that appears when the cursor is on a menu item. Also called a drop down list box.

questioning strategies: In these strategies a reader asks questions about a text before, during, and after reading and then searches for answers (e.g., Question Answer Response (QAR); Survey, Question, Read, Recite, Review (SQ3R)).

root words: Meaningful base form of a complex word, after all affixes are removed. A root may be independent, or free, as "read" in unreadable, or may be dependent, or bound, as *–liter–* (from the Greek word for letter) in illiterate.

sarcasm: A remark used to "make fun of" or "put down" someone or something. The remark is not sincere and is often intended to hurt someone's feelings.

scan: To examine or read something quickly, but selectively, for a purpose.

scanning: Examining or reading something quickly, but selectively, for a purpose.

schema: The accumulated knowledge drawn from life experiences that a person has to help understand concepts, roles, emotions, and events.

secondary sources: Sources of information that are derived from primary or original sources (e.g., gossip).

segment: The act of separating the sounds in a word in order to assist decoding or spelling.

semantic mapping: A graphic display of a cluster of words that are meaningfully related.

sentence structure: Any of a number of basic sentence types in a language. The pattern or structure of word order in sentences, clauses, or phrases.

sequence: The arrangement or ordering of information, content, or ideas (e.g., chronological, easy to difficult, part to whole).

sequential: Marked by an arrangement or order of information, content, or ideas, such as part to whole, easy to difficult, etc.

setting: The time(s) and place(s) in which a narrative takes place.

short vowel sounds: The sound of /a/ as in cat, /e/ as in hen, /i/ as in fit, /o/ as in hot, and /u/ as in pup.

sight words: Words that are immediately recognized as wholes and do not require word analysis for identification.

similes: Figures of speech comparing two unlike things usually using *like* or *as* (e.g., Like ancient trees, we die from the top).

skim: To read or glance through quickly.

story elements: The critical parts of a story, including character, setting, plot, problem, solution. At upper grades, the terms problem and solution change to conflict and resolution.

Glossary

story structure: The pattern of organization in narration that characterizes a particular type of story.

structural analysis: The identification of word-meaning elements, such as re- and read in reread, to help understand the meaning of a word as a whole.

sub-genres: Genres within other genres (e.g., haiku is a sub-genre of poetry, and mystery is a sub-genre of fiction).

subplot: A minor collection of events in a novel or drama that have some connection with the main plot and should (1) comment on, (2) complicate/defeat, or (3) support the main plot.

suffix: An affix attached to the end of a base, root, or stem that changes the meaning or grammatical function of the word (e.g., *-en* added to *ox* to form oxen).

summarize: To determine what is important in the text, condense this information, and put it into the students' own words.

summary: A synthesis of the important ideas in a text presented in a condensed form.

syllabication: Division of words into syllables. A syllable is a word part that contains a vowel, or in spoken language a vowel sound (e-vent; news-pa-per; ver-y).

synonym: A word having a meaning similar to that of another word.

task-oriented text: Text written specifically to direct the reader as to how to complete a task.

technical: Content or vocabulary directly related to specific knowledge or information in a career or interest area.

text complexity: Text demands on the reader increase substantially throughout the grades. Items that influence complexity of text include: highly specialized vocabulary and concepts; abstract concepts presented with minimal context; increased concept load/density; readability considerations; and unique writing patterns in informational text.

text features: A prominent characteristic of a particular type of text, such as chapter titles, sub-headings, and bold-faced words in a history text.

text organizational structures: Expository text is structured in certain ways. The five text structures that students are most likely to encounter are cause-effect, compare/contrast, description, problem/solution, and chronological or time order.

theme: A topic; a major idea or proposition broad enough to cover the entire scope of a literary work. Note: a theme may be stated or implicit, but clues to it may be found in the ideas that are given special prominence or tend to recur in a work.

unfamiliar text: Unseen, unpracticed reading material.

vocabulary strategies: A systematic plan to increase understanding of words (e.g., categorizing and classifying, semantic mapping, semantic feature analysis, concept of definition maps, analogies, using the dictionary and other reference materials, using word parts, using morphemic analysis, using context clues).

word families: A collection of words that share common orthographic rimes (e.g., thank, prank, dank).

word recognition strategies: Strategies for determining the pronunciation and meaning of words in print.

Reading Tutorial

The Reading Practice Tutorial is made up of multiple-choice and short-answer questions. These questions show you how the skills you have learned in Reading class may be tested on the Reading MSP. The questions also give you a chance to practice your skills. If you have trouble with a question, talk with a parent or teacher.

Read each question carefully. If you do not know an answer, you may skip the question and come back to it later.

When you finish, check your answers.

Directions for the Reading Tutorial

Today you will take the Reading Tutorial. You will read passages and answer questions. You may look back at the passage when you are answering the questions.

Directions to the Student

There are two different types of questions on this tutorial:

1. There are multiple-choice questions that require you to choose the best answer.

2. There are short-answer questions for which you will write phrases or sentences on the lines provided in your booklet.

Here are some important things to remember as you take this tutorial:

1. Read each passage. You may look back at the reading passage as often as you want.

2. The paragraphs are numbered for all reading passages. A question about a particular paragraph will refer to the paragraph number.

3. Read each question carefully. When you write your answers, write them neatly and clearly on the lines provided. You may use sentences, phrases, paragraphs, lists, or charts to explain your ideas. Cross out or erase any part of your work you do not want to include as part of your answer.

4. When you choose a multiple-choice answer, make sure you completely fill in the circle next to the answer. Erase completely any marks that you want to change on multiple-choice items.

5. Use only a **No. 2 pencil**, not a mechanical pencil or pen, to write your answers. If you do not have a No. 2 pencil, ask your teacher to give you one.

6. You should have plenty of time to finish every question on the tutorial. If you do not know the answer to a question, go on to the next question. You can come back to that question later.

7. When you reach the word **STOP** in your booklet, you have reached the end of the Tutorial. Do not go on until you are told to turn the page.

8. If you finish early, you may check your work in this session **only**.

Go on ▶

Sample Questions

To help you understand how to answer the test questions, look at the sample test questions below. These questions do not refer to the selections you are about to read. They are included to show you what the questions in the test are like and how to mark or write your answers.

Multiple-Choice Sample Question

For this type of question you will select the answer and fill in the circle next to it.

1   According to the story, what happens when the substitute teacher fills in for Mr. Scofield?

●   **A.**   The students learn to square dance.

○   **B.**   The students learn how to find the cafeteria.

○   **C.**   The students learn how to ski.

○   **D.**   The students learn how to play an instrument.

For this sample question, the correct answer is C; therefore, the circle next to C is filled in.

Short-Answer Sample Question

For this type of question you will write a short answer consisting of a few phrases or sentences.

2   What conclusion can the reader draw about Jack? Provide information from the story to support your conclusion.

Jack usually likes PE, but this year he dreads it.

Jack does not like to dance, and they are

learning to square dance in PE.

Go on ▶

Directions: Read the selection and answer the questions.

Riiiip!

1   At first glance, Velcro may seem to be a prime example of a synthetic creation. Generally made of nylon, a synthetic material, Velcro hardly seems like something one would find in the natural environment. But travel back to the beginnings of this noisy fastener, and you will find a beginning rooted entirely in nature.

2   In the 1940s, a Swiss engineer named George de Mestral was taking his dog for a walk. De Mestral spent a great deal of time outdoors, believing nature was an inspiration for formulating ideas for his work. On this particular day, he became intrigued with the large number of burrs stuck to his pants and to his dog's fur. Primarily, de Mestral wanted to understand how the burrs were able to hang on so stubbornly.

3   De Mestral examined the burrs under a microscope and noticed that each burr was made of hundreds of tiny hooks. When the hooks came in contact with something comprising loops, like fur, hair, or cloth, the hooks grabbed onto the loops, creating a fastening system that would not easily come undone on its own.

4   Alfred Gonet, a family friend of de Mestral's, thought the idea to turn this natural occurrence into an everyday, useful invention was a good one. So, de Mestral took his idea to cloth experts in France, who also liked the idea but were unsure if they could make it work. The challenge served as an inspiration to de Mestral, who undertook the task of weaving the fabric himself. After years of trial-and-error tests, he finally found a combination of hooks and loops that would fit together the same way the burrs would fit into fur and cloth.

5   In 1951, de Mestral filed to apply for a patent for his hook-and-loop fastener. Supported by Gonet & Co., he founded the Swiss company Velcro S.A., which eventually received patents in ten other countries, including the U.S.A. The name given to the company, Velcro, was formed by combining the French words for velvet (velour) and hook (crochet).

6   Velcro USA Inc., is currently the only producer of Velcro® brand hook and loop fasteners in the United States (other companies are allowed to make hook and loop fasteners, but they cannot use the brand name Velcro). Today, Velcro is used not only in clothing, shoes, backpacks, and toys, but also occasionally by doctors during surgeries and by astronauts to keep things from floating around inside space shuttles.

Go on ▶

1   What is the meaning of the word *synthetic* as it is used in paragraph 1 of the selection?

   ○ **A.**   Natural

   ○ **B.**   Authentic

   ○ **C.**   Basic

   ○ **D.**   Artificial

2   What is the main idea in the selection?

   ○ **A.**   The primary use of Velcro is to keep objects from floating around inside space shuttles.

   ○ **B.**   The idea for Velcro was inspired by the way burrs hook onto fur and clothing.

   ○ **C.**   The process of making Velcro is similar to the process of weaving fabric.

   ○ **D.**   The name "Velcro" is formed by combining the French words *velour* and *crochet*.

Go on ▶

3   Based on the information in the selection, why did de Mestral most likely decide to create Velcro? Include **two** details from the selection to support your answer.

_____

_____

_____

_____

_____

_____

_____

_____

Go on ▶

Copying is Prohibited
© Englefield & Associates, Inc.

4   Write a summary of the selection. Include **three** important events from the selection in your summary.

_____

_____

_____

_____

_____

_____

_____

_____

Go on ➤

Directions: Read the story and answer the questions.

The Old House

Part I: Leaving the Woods

1   I emerged at the far end of the dirt path, just past the line of trees. The old house loomed not more than a hundred yards beyond. I expected that it might look smaller, or at least less ominous, now that I was a few years older and wasn't so caught up in silly, youthful superstition. But this was not the case; it had only acquired more cracks and gaps and broken boards to add to its enormous, run-down appearance.

2   Back in elementary school, my friend Jack and I had passed this house almost every day on our way home from school. Some days, we ran past as quickly as we could, convinced that something inside was going to get us. Other days, we explored, daring each other to peek through broken windows and holes in the siding. The middle school we attend now is farther away, so we carpool. Today, though, Jack was sick, and my mom had to pick up her friend from the airport. It was a cold and snowy day, but with the only alternative being a two-hour wait for my mom to pick me up, I chose the walk.

3   As I approached the house, I drifted in my course so that I was walking in the large vacant yard that separated the house from the sidewalk. Feeling almost as if some external force was compelling me to do so, I angled my path closer and closer to the abandoned structure. The contrast between the dinginess of the house and the bright white snow gave it a surreal quality.

Part II: An Unfamiliar Noise

4   A minute or two later, I found myself only a few feet away from the house. I tiptoed around the perimeter, peering in windows. The inside was exactly as I remembered it—broken and rotting wood furniture, everything covered in a thick coat of dust. I was staring so intently that I didn't see the gigantic icicle beginning to break free from the overhang just to my right.

5   SNAP! WHOOSH! THUD! A noise unlike any I had ever heard sounded above my head, only a few feet away. My heart jumped into my throat, and I instinctively began running as fast as I could. After a few seconds, I glanced back over my shoulder and saw the huge chunk of ice still trembling where it had landed in the snow. Knowing the cause of the noise, I slowed my pace slightly, but the event had jarred my thoughts; I wanted to get off that particular street as quickly as I could.

Go on ▶

© Englefield & Associates, Inc.

6   Still running, I reached the end of the block and burst out onto the main street through town. I stopped and looked around—everyone was going about their tasks, paying no attention to me standing on the corner, trying to catch my breath. I stood up straight and began to walk again. By the time I reached my street, I was laughing out loud at my childish fright. I decided to call Jack when I got home; I knew he would get a laugh out of the situation, too.

Go on ▶

5   Which idea is included in the section titled **An Unfamiliar Noise**?

○ **A.**   The narrator finds that the inside of the house is the same as he remembers it.

○ **B.**   The narrator believes the house might seem smaller now that he is older.

○ **C.**   The narrator thinks that the contrast of the house with the snow gives the house a surreal quality.

○ **D.**   The narrator feels as if some type of force is pulling him closer to the house.

6   How does the narrator feel about the old house?

○ **A.**   Terrified

○ **B.**   Curious

○ **C.**   Uninterested

○ **D.**   Obsessed

Go on ▶

7   Which sentence explains why the narrator starts laughing at the end of the story?

     O **A.**   He sees someone driving by in a funny-looking car.

     O **B.**   He remembers a joke Jack told him when they were younger.

     O **C.**   He is amused by his childish reaction to the icicle falling.

     O **D.**   He is running so fast that he trips over the sidewalk and falls.

8   Which sentence from the story is an example of imagery?

     O **A.**   "A minute or two later, I found myself only a few feet away from the house."

     O **B.**   "It had only acquired more cracks and gaps and broken boards to add to its enormous, run-down appearance."

     O **C.**   "I stopped and looked around—everyone was going about their tasks, paying no attention to me standing on the corner, trying to catch my breath."

     O **D.**   "Today, though, Jack was sick, and my mom had to pick up her friend from the airport."

Go on ▶

Directions: Read the selection and answer the questions.

How to Make Pretzels

1   You may know pretzels as a quick snack you might buy at the pool, at a basketball game, or in bags from the store. Did you know, however, that you can make these simple treats on your own? It's not as hard as you might think. It doesn't take much time to do, and you probably have a lot of the ingredients around the house already.

2   First, you need a large mixing bowl; to this bowl, you will add one and a half cups of warm water. Test the temperature of the water by sticking a (clean) finger in it— the water shouldn't be so hot that you can't comfortably hold your finger in it. If the water is too hot, it will kill the yeast, which is an essential component to making the dough.

3   Next, sprinkle two teaspoons of dry yeast into the water and let the yeast dissolve. After about five minutes, the water-yeast mixture should start to bubble. When it does, it means you are ready to go on with the recipe. If the mixture never bubbles, this means the yeast is most likely stale and the dough will not form correctly.

4   Once the mixture bubbles, add one tablespoon of sugar to the bowl. This sugar is the defining factor that makes the recipe appropriate for pretzels instead of for bread. The sugar lets you work with the dough without having to wait for it to rise. At this point, you will also add one teaspoon of melted butter and one and a half teaspoons of salt.

5   The final ingredient to add is the flour. Using a wooden spoon, mix three and a half cups of flour into the bowl and stir it until it becomes too difficult to stir anymore. Now, turn the bowl over, and dump out the dough onto a well-floured board. Knead the dough by doubling it over and then pushing it down and out with your palms. While kneading the dough, it is important to remember that you don't want to tear it; you just want to stretch it out.

Go on ▶

6   After you have kneaded the dough for a few minutes and it is stretched somewhat flat, cut it into eight or ten long, thin sections, depending on how large you want the finished pretzels to be. Roll them around until they are snakelike in appearance. Bend each of these sections into a traditional pretzel shape or any other shape you like. When you have shaped all of the sections, brush the pretzels using a mixture of one egg yolk and one teaspoon of water. After the pretzels are covered with the yolk mixture, sprinkle each one with coarse salt. If you want to try something different, you could also use poppy seeds or sesame seeds, or leave the pretzel plain.

7   To bake your homemade pretzels, preheat an oven to 425 degrees. Make sure you have permission to use the oven, or have an adult preheat the oven for you. Now, take a cookie sheet and cover it with foil, facing the shiny side of the foil down. Place the pretzels on the cookie sheet and bake for 15 minutes. You might want to set a timer so you don't cook the pretzels for too long and burn them. When the timer goes off, voilà—you have a tasty, homemade snack to share with your family and friends.

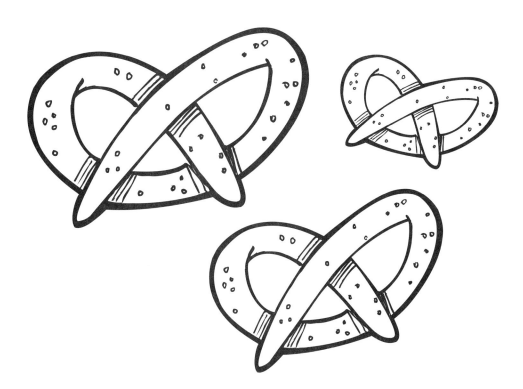

Go on ▶

9   One conclusion that a reader can draw from this selection is that making your own pretzels is easy. Provide **two** details from the selection to support this conclusion.

_____

_____

_____

_____

_____

_____

_____

Go on ▶

 © Englefield & Associates, Inc.

10 The author's purpose for writing this selection may have been to teach the reader how to make homemade pretzels. Provide **two** details from the selection to support this purpose.

_____

_____

_____

_____

_____

_____

_____

_____

Go on ▶

11 Which sentence best describes the author's feelings about making pretzels in the selection?

    ○ **A.**   "To bake your homemade pretzels, preheat an oven to 425 degrees."

    ○ **B.**   "This sugar is the defining factor that makes the recipe appropriate for pretzels instead of for bread."

    ○ **C.**   "When you have shaped all of the sections, brush the pretzels using a mixture of one egg yolk and one teaspoon of water."

    ○ **D.**   "It doesn't take much time to do, and you probably have a lot of the ingredients around the house already."

12 Which word best describes the author's tone in this selection?

    ○ **A.**   Instructive

    ○ **B.**   Persuasive

    ○ **C.**   Sympathetic

    ○ **D.**   Humorous

Go on ▶

Directions: Read the poem and answer the questions.

Give Me the Splendid Silent Sun
Walt Whitman

1

GIVE me the splendid silent sun with all his beams full-dazzling,
Give me juicy autumnal fruit ripe and red from the orchard,
Give me a field where the unmow'd grass grows,
Give me an arbor, give me the trellis'd[1] grape,
5   Give me fresh corn and wheat, give me serene-moving animals teaching content,
Give me nights perfectly quiet as on high plateaus west of the Mississippi, and
       I looking up at the stars,
Give me odorous[2] at sunrise a garden of beautiful flowers where I
       can walk undisturb'd,
Give me for marriage a sweet-breath'd woman of whom I should
       never tire,
Give me a perfect child, give me away aside from the noise of the
       world a rural domestic life,
10   Give me to warble spontaneous songs recluse[3] by myself, for my
       own ears only,
Give me solitude, give me Nature, give me again O Nature your
       primal sanities!
These demanding to have them (tired with ceaseless excitement,
       and rack'd by the war-strife[4]),
These to procure[5] incessantly[6] asking, rising in cries from
       my heart,

While yet incessantly asking still I
       adhere to my city,
15   Day upon day and year upon year O
       city, walking your streets,
Where you hold me enchain'd a certain
       time refusing to give me up,
Yet giving to make me glutted[7], enrich'd of
       soul, you give me forever faces;
(Oh I see what I sought to escape,
       confronting, reversing my cries,
I see my own soul trampling down what it
       ask'd for).

---

[1]*trellis: an arch used as a support for vines and other creeping plants*
[2]*odorous: having a distinct odor*
[3]*recluse: withdrawn from the world*
[4]*strife: a conflict; a violent struggle*
[5]*procure: to obtain or acquire*
[6]*incessantly: continuing without interruption*
[7]*glutted: filled beyond capacity*

Go on ▶

2

20 Keep your splendid silent sun,
     Keep your woods O Nature, and the quiet places by the woods,
     Keep your fields of clover and timothy[8], and your corn-fields and orchards,
     Keep the blossoming buckwheat fields where the Ninth-month bees hum;
     Give me faces and streets—give me these phantoms incessant and endless along the
          trottoirs[9]!
25 Give me interminable[10] eyes—give me women—give me comrades and lovers by
          the thousand!
     Let me see new ones every day—let me hold new ones by the hand every day!
     Give me such shows—give me the streets of Manhattan!
     Give me Broadway, with the soldiers marching—give me the sound of the trumpets
          and drums!
     (The soldiers in companies or regiments—some starting away, flush'd and reckless,
30 Some, their time up, returning with thinn'd ranks, young, yet very old, worn,
          marching, noticing nothing;)
     Give me the shores and wharves[11] heavy-fringed with black ships!
     O such for me! O an intense life, full to repletion[12] and varied!
     The life of the theatre, bar-room, huge hotel, for me!
     The saloon of the steamer! the crowded excursion for me! the torchlight procession!
35 The dense brigade bound for the war, with high piled military wagons following;
     People, endless, streaming, with strong voices, passions, pageants,
     Manhattan streets with their powerful throbs,
               with beating drums as now,
     The endless and noisy chorus, the rustle and
               clank of muskets (even the sight of
               the wounded),
     Manhattan crowds, with their turbulent
               musical chorus!
40 Manhattan faces and eyes forever for me.

---

[8]timothy: a North American grass

[9]trottoir: footpath; sidewalk

[10]interminable: seeming to be without an end

[11]wharves: landing places for ships

[12]repletion: being fully satisfied or completely filled

Go on ▶

13 Based on the information in the poem, which generalization can the reader make about living in the city?

     ○ **A.** It is a hectic lifestyle.

     ○ **B.** The city provides a tranquil atmosphere.

     ○ **C.** City life is only for the wealthy.

     ○ **D.** Living in the city is depressing.

14 How are the narrator in section 1 of the poem and the narrator in section 2 of the poem similar?

     ○ **A.** Both enjoy the sounds of trumpets and drums.

     ○ **B.** Both enjoy looking up at the stars at night.

     ○ **C.** Both are looking for a setting in which to live a happy life.

     ○ **D.** Both are looking to spend the rest of their lives in a quiet, sunny place.

Go on ▶

15 The author of the poem seems to believe that "some people enjoy spending time in nature, while others enjoy fast-paced cities."

Do you agree with this statement? Support your answer with **two** details from the poem.

_____

_____

_____

_____

_____

_____

_____

_____

STOP

© Englefield & Associates, Inc.

Reading Assessment One

Introduction

Reading Assessment One is made up of multiple-choice and short-answer questions. These questions show you how the skills you have learned in Reading class may be tested on the Reading MSP. The questions also give you a chance to practice your skills. If you have trouble with a question, talk with a parent or teacher.

Read each question carefully. If you do not know an answer, you may skip the question and come back to it later.

When you finish, check your answers.

Directions for the Reading Assessment One

Today you will take the Reading Assessment One. You will read passages and answer questions. You may look back at the passage when you are answering the questions.

Directions to the Student

There are two different types of questions on this assessment:

1. There are multiple-choice questions that require you to choose the best answer.

2. There are short-answer questions for which you will write phrases or sentences on the lines provided in your booklet.

Here are some important things to remember as you take this assessment:

1. Read each passage. You may look back at the reading passage as often as you want.

2. The paragraphs are numbered for all reading passages. A question about a particular paragraph will refer to the paragraph number.

3. Read each question carefully. When you write your answers, write them neatly and clearly on the lines provided. You may use sentences, phrases, paragraphs, lists, or charts to explain your ideas. Cross out or erase any part of your work you do not want to include as part of your answer.

4. When you choose a multiple-choice answer, make sure you completely fill in the circle next to the answer. Erase completely any marks that you want to change on multiple-choice items.

5. Use only a **No. 2 pencil**, not a mechanical pencil or pen, to write your answers. If you do not have a No. 2 pencil, ask your teacher to give you one.

6. You should have plenty of time to finish every question on the assessment. If you do not know the answer to a question, go on to the next question. You can come back to that question later.

7. When you reach the word **STOP** in your booklet, you have reached the end of Assessment One. Do not go on until you are told to turn the page.

8. If you finish early, you may check your work in this session **only**.

Go on ▶

Directions: Read the story and answer the questions.

Alice in Wonderland
By Lewis Carroll

1   The rabbit-hole went straight on like a tunnel for some way, and then dipped suddenly down, so suddenly that Alice had not a moment to think about stopping herself before she found herself falling down a very deep well.

2   Either the well was very deep, or she fell very slowly, for she had plenty of time as she went down to look about her and to wonder what was going to happen next. First, she tried to look down and make out what she was coming to, but it was too dark to see anything; then she looked at the sides of the well, and noticed that they were filled with cupboards and book-shelves; here and there she saw maps and pictures hung upon pegs. She took down a jar from one of the shelves as she passed; it was labeled 'ORANGE MARMALADE', but to her great disappointment it was empty: she did not like to drop the jar for fear of killing somebody, so managed to put it into one of the cupboards as she fell past it.

3   'Well!' thought Alice to herself, 'after such a fall as this, I shall think nothing of tumbling down stairs! How brave they'll all think me at home! Why, I wouldn't say anything about it, even if I fell off the top of the house!' (Which was very likely true.)

4   Down, down, down. Would the fall NEVER come to an end! 'I wonder how many miles I've fallen by this time?' she said aloud. 'I must be getting somewhere near the centre of the earth. Let me see: that would be four thousand miles down, I think—' (for, you see, Alice had learnt several things of this sort in her lessons in the schoolroom, and though this was not a VERY good opportunity for showing off her knowledge, as there was no one to listen to her, still it was good practice to say it over) '—yes, that's about the right distance—but then I wonder what Latitude or Longitude I've got to?' (Alice had no idea what Latitude was, or Longitude either, but thought they were nice grand words to say.)

Go on ▶

5   Presently she began again. 'I wonder if I shall fall right THROUGH the earth!
How funny it'll seem to come out among the people that walk with their heads
downward! The Antipathies, I think—' (she was rather glad there WAS no one
listening, this time, as it didn't sound at all the right word) '—but I shall have to ask
them what the name of the country is, you know. Please, Ma'am, is this New Zealand
or Australia?' (and she tried to curtsey as she spoke—fancy CURTSEYING as you're
falling through the air! Do you think you could manage it?) 'And what an ignorant
little girl she'll think me for asking! No, it'll never do to ask: perhaps I shall see it
written up somewhere.'

6   Down, down, down. There was
nothing else to do, so Alice soon
began talking again. 'Dinah'll miss
me very much to-night, I should
think!' (Dinah was the cat.) 'I hope
they'll remember her saucer of
milk at tea-time. Dinah my dear! I
wish you were down here with me!
There are no mice in the air, I'm
afraid, but you might catch a bat,
and that's very like a mouse, you
know. But do cats eat bats, I
wonder?' And here Alice began to
get rather sleepy, and went on
saying to herself, in a dreamy sort
of way, 'Do cats eat bats? Do cats
eat bats?' and sometimes, 'Do bats
eat cats?' for, you see, as she
couldn't answer either question, it
didn't much matter which way she
put it. She felt that she was dozing
off, and had just begun to dream
that she was walking hand in hand
with Dinah, and saying to her very
earnestly, 'Now, Dinah, tell me the
truth: did you ever eat a bat?'
when suddenly, thump! thump!
down she came upon a heap of
sticks and dry leaves, and the fall
was over.

Go on ▶

1 What is the main idea of the story? Support your answer with **one** example from the story.

_____

_____

_____

_____

_____

_____

_____

_____

2 Based on the information in the story, what do you predict Alice will do now that she has stopped falling?

○ **A.** She will try to find her cat, Dinah.

○ **B.** She will try to find out where she is.

○ **C.** She will try to climb up out of the well.

○ **D.** She will try to find out what cats eat.

Go on ➤

3 Which sentence best summarizes this story?

○ **A.** A girl named Alice is trying to learn about Australia and New Zealand, so she intentionally falls down a hole that she thinks will take her to one of those places.

○ **B.** A girl named Alice finds a jar of orange marmalade; however, it is empty, so she tries to find a place to put it.

○ **C.** A girl named Alice wonders what type of food cats like and what she will feed her cat when she returns home.

○ **D.** A girl named Alice falls down a deep hole, and she thinks of many different things while she is falling, including her cat and where she is going to find herself at the end of the fall.

4 Which sentence from the story is an example of exaggeration?

○ **A.** " 'I must be getting somewhere near the centre of the earth. Let me see: that would be four thousand miles down, I think.' "

○ **B.** "There was nothing else to do, so Alice soon began talking again."

○ **C.** "Either the well was very deep, or she fell very slowly, for she had plenty of time as she went down to look about her and to wonder what was going to happen next."

○ **D.** " 'Well!' thought Alice to herself, 'after such a fall as this, I shall think nothing of tumbling down stairs!' "

Go on ▶

 © Englefield & Associates, Inc.

5 Which sentence tells how the beginning of Alice's fall and the end of her fall are different?

     ○ **A.** At the beginning of her fall, she is interested in knowing where she is; by the end, she is no longer interested.

     ○ **B.** At the beginning of the fall, she is asleep; she wakes up when she nears the end of the fall.

     ○ **C.** At the beginning of the fall, she is thinking about her cat; at the end of the fall, she is wondering where she is.

     ○ **D.** At the beginning of the fall, Alice is concerned with her surroundings; at the end of the fall, she is thinking about her cat.

6 What is the author's purpose for writing the story?

     ○ **A.** To entertain readers with a story about a girl

     ○ **B.** To describe to readers how a girl talks to her cat

     ○ **C.** To inform readers about falling down a hole

     ○ **D.** To persuade readers to dream about falling

7 Which word best describes the author's tone in this story?

     ○ **A.** Humorous

     ○ **B.** Formal

     ○ **C.** Impersonal

     ○ **D.** Angry

Go on ➤

Directions: Read the selection and answer the questions.

Centralia

The Founder

1   In the context of history, the name George Washington is a familiar one. The George Washington who founded a city in the Pacific Northwest, however, is a lesser-known historical figure, but still a highly important one. This George Washington was born in Virginia in 1817 to a slave and an English woman. When his father was sold to a new owner, Washington's mother took him to live with a couple, the Cochranes, who eventually adopted him and taught him to read, write, and do arithmetic.

2   Washington left home at 24, but journeys to Missouri and Illinois quickly taught him that many people were not accepting of a free, property-owning black man. Frustrated, he decided to see whether the Pacific Northwest would be a more welcoming environment, and the Cochranes opted to accompany him. Washington found a spot at the junction of the Skookumchuck and Chehalis Rivers that was perfect for a settlement, so Jim Cochrane filed for ownership of the land.

A Town's Beginnings

3   The Cochranes acted as owners of the land until 1853, when the laws changed to allow black men to own land. Washington paid Cochrane for the original land purchase; then, he bought 63 additional acres to add to his claim.

4   By 1872, the Northern Pacific Railway had been established next to Washington's land up to the Chehalis River to the north. Washington perceived this as a good time to start a town. He filed his intention with the territory's auditor to lay out a town called "Centerville," with lots selling for $10.00 each.

5   Everyone who purchased a lot in Centerville had to promise to construct a building valued at no less than $100. Later, to attract more settlers, Washington doubled the size of the lots he sold. When the town, as part of Washington state, entered the Union in 1889, it had close to 1,000 residents. A mere two years later, the number was verging on 2,000.

6   The town's citizens became tired of having Centerville confused with so many other towns of the same name, so they called a public meeting. A new arrival from Centralia, Illinois, convinced the other residents to rename the city after his former hometown.

Go on ▶

Depression and Recovery

7   When an economic depression hit in 1893, George Washington was the savior of the town. He made 85-mile trips in a wagon to get supplies for the townspeople, and he bought these supplies with his own money. He lent money, interest-free, and gave people as long as they needed to pay him back. And to save his town from bankruptcy, he bought any of the town's property that went up for auction himself.

8   Washington's investments paid off. By 1900, the crisis had passed, and he was well respected and financially secure. He continued to plan for the town's future until his death at 88, in 1905. The mayor of Centralia called for a town-wide day of mourning. Washington's funeral—the biggest in Centralia's history—was held at a church he helped build, on ground that he had donated to his city.

Go on ▶

8   What is the meaning of the word *junction* as it is used in paragraph 2 of the selection?

   ○ **A.**   Point in time

   ○ **B.**   Intersection

   ○ **C.**   Layer of metal

   ○ **D.**   Road

9   What is the purpose of the subtitles?

   ○ **A.**   To break the information into section's related by topic

   ○ **B.**   To present a timeline of the selection's events

   ○ **C.**   To help the reader understand where Centralia is located

   ○ **D.**   To paint an image of the town for the reader

Go on ▶

10 Based on the information in the selection, which conclusion can the reader draw about George Washington?

○ **A.** Washington is trying to learn more about the Chehalis River.

○ **B.** Washington is trying to overcome an obstacle to reach a goal.

○ **C.** Washington is learning about different types of houses in the 1800s.

○ **D.** Washington is curious about the Northern Pacific Railway.

11 According to the selection, what happens when George Washington faces the problem of his town being in an economic depression?

○ **A.** He buys supplies, gives loans, and buys bankrupted properties.

○ **B.** He establishes the Northern Pacific Railway.

○ **C.** He makes trips in his wagon to purchase supplies.

○ **D.** He moves in with the Cochranes to learn to read, write, and do arithmetic.

Go on ►

12 Which sentence from the selection is an opinion?

○ **A.** "By 1900, the crisis had passed, and he was well-respected and financially secure."

○ **B.** "Everyone who purchased a lot in Centerville had to promise to construct a building valued at no less than $100."

○ **C.** "Washington perceived this as a good time to start a town."

○ **D.** "The George Washington who founded a city in the Pacific Northwest, however, is a lesser-known historical figure, but still a highly important one."

13 Which sentence best explains why George Washington moved to the Pacific Northwest?

○ **A.** "Washington left home at 24, but journeys to Missouri and Illinois quickly taught him that many people were not accepting of a free, property-owning black man."

○ **B.** "By 1872, the Northern Pacific Railway had been established next to Washington's land up to the Chehalis River to the north."

○ **C.** "When his father was sold to a new owner, Washington's mother took him to live with a couple, the Cochranes, who eventually adopted him and taught him to read, write, and do arithmetic."

○ **D.** "Washington found a spot at the junction of the Skookumchuck and Chehalis Rivers that was perfect for a settlement, so Jim Cochrane filed for ownership of the land."

Go on ▶

14 Which statement is the most important conclusion the reader may draw from the selection?

   ○ **A.**   George Washington showed determination when he rode 85 miles to get supplies.

   ○ **B.**   Jim Cochrane showed determination when he bought land for Washington.

   ○ **C.**   George Washington showed determination when he founded a town and kept it running through an economic depression.

   ○ **D.**   The townspeople of Centralia showed determination when they built houses worth at least $100.

Go on ▶

Directions: Read the selection and answer the questions.

Beyond Color

1   Mention the word "astronomer," and you will generally conjure an image of a person with a telescope. Whether it's an amateur astronomer using a small telescope in a backyard or a professional with an enormous version in an observatory, the idea of an astronomer typically goes hand in hand with this instrument that helps him or her magnify faraway objects.

2   Recent astronomers, however, have found that there is much more to the universe than that which can be seen with even the aided eye. In the 1980s, astronomers began to study space using an exciting development known as infrared radiation. Infrared radiation is heat given off by objects that is outside the range of wavelengths that humans see as colors. Some objects in space that are not visible to the eye because they are hidden by clouds of gas and dust, give off infrared waves that are able to pass through these barriers.

3   Using satellites, astronomers can put infrared telescopes into space to pick up some of the infrared radiation given off by objects in the universe. At certain wavelengths of infrared, the dust in space becomes almost transparent, and stars that are too small and cool to be seen through a telescope show up.

4   Stars are not the only objects that are easier to view using infrared; some galaxies, particle clouds, molecules, and even planets can be detected with infrared. If a planet or some other object in space is near a bright star, the brightness of the star will often make any objects around it difficult to see. In infrared wavelengths, however, the star's brightness is diminished, and the nearby object becomes easier to find.

5   For many objects in space, infrared astronomy is an important component of getting a more complete image. It is similar to adding specific details to a painting that only shows basic outlines. It also enables astronomers to find objects they would never otherwise be able to see. With many infrared projects planned for the future, it is likely that infrared will help astronomers learn much more about the universe we live in.

Go on ▶

© Englefield & Associates, Inc.

15 What is the meaning of the word *conjure* as it is used in paragraph 1 of the selection?

　　○ **A.**　To perform magic

　　○ **B.**　To appeal to

　　○ **C.**　To forget

　　○ **D.**　To bring to mind

16 The selection shows that infrared has become a useful tool to astronomers in recent years. Provide **two** details from the selection that support this idea.

_____

_____

_____

_____

_____

_____

_____

_____

Go on▶

17 Which sentence from the selection is an opinion?

    ○ **A.** "Infrared radiation is heat given off by objects that is outside the range of wavelengths that humans see as colors."

    ○ **B.** "Mention the word 'astronomer,' and you will generally conjure an image of a person with a telescope."

    ○ **C.** "In infrared wavelengths, however, the star's brightness is diminished, and the nearby object becomes easier to find."

    ○ **D.** "Using satellites, astronomers can put infrared telescopes into space to pick up some of the infrared radiation given off by objects in the universe."

18 In paragraph 2 of the selection, why does the author include a description of how infrared works in the field of astronomy?

    ○ **A.** So readers will understand how astronomers are using infrared to their advantage

    ○ **B.** So readers will know that infrared is a tool only useful to astronomers

    ○ **C.** So readers will understand that infrared has very little use in astronomy

    ○ **D.** So readers will be aware that all satellites use infrared technology

Go on ▶

19 What inference can you make about using infrared technology in the field of astronomy?

○ **A.**   Stars are easier to see using a telescope.

○ **B.**   Astronomers are not using infrared technology.

○ **C.**   Infrared enables astronomers to see things they can't normally see.

○ **D.**   Astronomers have many projects planned for the future.

Go on ▶

Directions: Read the story and answer the questions.

Morning at the Fort

1   I awoke at dawn, at the point when the sunlight was a scarcely visible glow in the eastern sky. In the darkness of early morning, the cold was apparent, and so I added a knit hat and blanket over my standard wardrobe of buckskin leggings, calico shirt, buckskin hunting shirt, and moccasins. Over the last layer, I added my buckskin belt, and to that affixed my knife, sheath, and pouch.

2   As I made my final preparations to leave the camp, I looked over at my sleeping wife and son. Although they slept now, they would wake soon and find themselves busy with the customary tasks: cleaning and tanning skins; repairing clothing and shoes; hunting, harvesting, and cooking meals; and foremost of all, guarding the camp while I was out on brigade.

3   I encountered on my way to the Fort many other men such as myself—short and muscular, with roughly lined faces from so much exposure to the elements. Most were clothed as I myself was, and many were wearing colorful, handwoven sashes. The cheerfulness of these garments would generally seem a contrast to such gruff-looking men, but instead, this juxtaposition alerted you to the cheerfulness and satisfaction lurking beneath the exterior coarseness of the skin, bringing you to the inescapable conclusion: these men loved what they did. All of us—every single one—loved going out on the brigade.

Go on ▶

20 According to the story, what happens when the hunters are away from camp?

○ **A.**   Family members who stay behind must take care of all camp work, including guarding the camp.

○ **B.**   Family members must eventually go out and find the hunters and bring them back home.

○ **C.**   Family members do nothing except sit around camp and wait for the hunters to return.

○ **D.**   Family members leave on their own expeditions and do not come back until the hunters have already returned.

21 Based on the information in the story, which generalization can the reader make about going out on the brigade?

○ **A.**   No one ever returns to the camp once the brigade leaves.

○ **B.**   It is a long and often difficult journey that includes exposure to danger.

○ **C.**   It is a daylong trip down the coast to obtain supplies.

○ **D.**   People who went out on brigade were not prepared for the task.

22 Based on the information in the story, what conclusion can the reader draw about the narrator?

○ **A.**   He is unmotivated and lazy.

○ **B.**   He is not interested in working at the fort for much longer.

○ **C.**   He is well prepared and motivated for the upcoming task.

○ **D.**   He believes that his job is more important than the jobs others do at the fort.

Go on ▶

23 Based on the information in the story, what conclusion can the reader draw about the setting?

    ○ **A.**   The story takes place in the winter.

    ○ **B.**   The story takes place in the south.

    ○ **C.**   The story takes place at a sawmill.

    ○ **D.**   The story takes place in London.

24 Which word could the author have used in paragraph 2 instead of *customary*?

    ○ **A.**   Unusual

    ○ **B.**   Scarce

    ○ **C.**   Strange

    ○ **D.**   Common

Go on ▶

FORT VANCOUVER

- Established in 1825 on the north bank of the Columbia River
- Was the first European outpost in the Pacific Northwest
- Built to oversee operations of the Hudson's Bay Company—a fur-trading company based in London—in the western part of the country
- Grew quickly in its early years, encompassing approximately 300 square miles that contained grazing areas, gardens, orchards, sawmills, and dairies (among other things)
- Allowed little European settlement in areas surrounding the fort
- Became an end point for Americans migrating west; Hudson's Bay Company found itself giving the settlers supplies and employment so they wouldn't become competitors
- The U.S. Army established a base near Fort Vancouver in 1849, bringing more American settlers.
- Hudson's Bay Company moved its headquarters north in 1849 and moved out of Fort Vancouver completely in 1860.
- The fort, located in Vancouver, Washington, is now a National Historic Site.

25 In the selection, why does the author include the technique of presenting the information as bullet points?

   ○ **A.** Because the information is not presented in chronological order, and this format makes the information easier to rearrange

   ○ **B.** Because it separates each fact from the next and makes individual facts easier to find

   ○ **C.** Because none of the facts are about similar topics, so it would be impossible to put them in paragraph form

   ○ **D.** Because each point describes a step in how the fort was built, so it makes sense to arrange them this way

26 According to the fourth bullet point which statement is true?

   ○ **A.** The fort was located on the south bank of the Columbia River.

   ○ **B.** The fort contained fountains and swimming pools.

   ○ **C.** The fort encompassed more than 500 square miles.

   ○ **D.** The fort contained gardens and orchards.

27 Based on the information in the selection, what assumption can the reader make about typical occurrences at the fort today?

   ○ **A.** People can visit the fort to get an idea of what it was like more than 100 years ago.

   ○ **B.** The fort no longer exists; it was torn down when Hudson's Bay Company moved.

   ○ **C.** Hudson's Bay Company still uses the fort for some of its operations today.

   ○ **D.** The fort has been forgotten and is no longer used for any purpose.

Go on ▶

28 What is the main difference between how information about the fort is presented in the two selections?

   ○ **A.** "Facts About Fort Vancouver" gives more descriptive information about the fort itself, while "Morning at the Fort" gives historical background.

   ○ **B.** "Facts About Fort Vancouver" gives historical information about the fort, while "Morning at the Fort" gives a timeline of the fort.

   ○ **C.** "Facts About Fort Vancouver" gives a timeline of the fort, while "Morning at the Fort" gives a physical description of the fort's appearance.

   ○ **D.** "Facts About Fort Vancouver" gives factual background information about the fort itself, while "Morning at the Fort" gives a brief description of a person's life there.

29 The author of "Facts About Fort Vancouver" states that the fort was "Built to oversee operations of the Hudson's Bay Company—a fur-trading company based in London—in the western part of the country." Provide **two** examples from "Morning at the Fort" that demonstrate that Fort Vancouver was a base for a fur-trading company.

_____

_____

_____

_____

_____

_____

_____

_____

Go on‣

Directions: Read the selection and answer the questions.

OF THE ORIGIN AND DESIGN OF GOVERNMENT IN GENERAL
From "Common Sense," 1776
By Thomas Paine

1   Some writers have so confounded society with government, as to leave little or no distinction between them; whereas they are not only different, but have different origins. Society is produced by our wants, and government by wickedness; the former promotes our happiness positively by uniting our affections, the latter negatively by restraining our vices. The one encourages intercourse, the other creates distinctions. The first is a patron, the last a punisher.

2   Society in every state is a blessing, but government even in its best state is but a necessary evil; in its worst state an intolerable one; for when we suffer, or are exposed to the same miseries by a government, which we might expect in a country without government, our calamity is heightened by reflecting that we furnish the means by which we suffer. Government, like dress, is the badge of lost innocence; the palaces of kings are built on the ruins of the bowers of paradise. For were the impulses of conscience clear, uniform, and irresistibly obeyed, man would need no other lawgiver; but that not being the case, he finds it necessary to surrender up a part of his property to furnish means for the protection of the rest; and this he is induced to do by the same prudence which in every other case advises him out of two evils to choose the least. Wherefore, security being the true design and end of government, it unanswerably follows that whatever form thereof appears most likely to ensure it to us, with the least expence and greatest benefit, is preferable to all others.

3   In order to gain a clear and just idea of the design and end of government, let us suppose a small number of persons settled in some sequestered part of the earth, unconnected with the rest, they will then represent the first peopling of any country, or of the world. In this state of natural liberty, society will be their first thought. A thousand motives will excite them thereto, the strength of one man is so unequal to his wants, and his mind so unfitted for perpetual solitude, that he is soon obliged to seek assistance and relief of another, who in his turn requires the same. Four or five united would be able to raise a tolerable dwelling in the midst of a wilderness, but one man might labour out the common period of life without accomplishing any thing; when he had felled his timber he could not remove it, nor erect it after it was removed; hunger in the mean time would urge him from his work, and every different want call him a different way. Disease, nay even misfortune would be death, for though neither might be mortal, yet either would disable him from living, and reduce him to a state in which he might rather be said to perish than to die.

Go on ►

30 The author of the selection states, "Society in every state is a blessing, but government even in its best state is but a necessary evil…" Do you agree with his statement? Support your answer with **two** details from the selection.

_____

_____

_____

_____

_____

_____

_____

_____

31 Based on the information in the selection, what inference can the reader make about the author?

○ **A.** He would support the idea of the government having a larger role in people's lives.

○ **B.** He has no interest in what the government does.

○ **C.** He believes there is no reason that governments should exist.

○ **D.** He would not support the idea of the government having a larger role in people's lives.

Go on ▶

32 What is the meaning of the word *confounded* as it is used in paragraph 1 of the selection?

   ○ **A.** Discovered

   ○ **B.** Lost

   ○ **C.** Confused

   ○ **D.** Horrified

33 What is the main idea of the selection?

   ○ **A.** Man no longer needs the government.

   ○ **B.** Society promotes happiness.

   ○ **C.** Government is unnecessary.

   ○ **D.** Government is necessary.

Go on ▶

34 What is the purpose of the title "Common Sense"?

    ○ **A.**   Thomas Paine wrote in a style that everyone could understand.

    ○ **B.**   Thomas Paine wanted all people to have independence.

    ○ **C.**   Thomas Paine wrote in a style that only government could understand.

    ○ **D.**   Thomas Paine wanted all people to know that government was necessary.

Go on ▶

35 In paragraph 3 of the selection, why does the author include the example of a small group of people unconnected with the rest of the earth? Include **two** details from the selection in your answer.

_____

_____

_____

_____

_____

_____

_____

_____

STOP

Reading Assessment Two

Introduction

Reading Assessment Two is made up of multiple-choice and short-answer questions. These questions show you how the skills you have learned in Reading class may be tested on the Reading MSP. The questions also give you a chance to practice your skills. If you have trouble with a question, talk with a parent or teacher.

Read each question carefully. If you do not know an answer, you may skip the question and come back to it later.

When you finish, check your answers.

Directions for the Reading Assessment Two

Today you will take the Reading Assessment Two. You will read passages and answer questions. You may look back at the passage when you are answering the questions.

Directions to the Student

There are two different types of questions on this assessment:

1. There are multiple-choice questions that require you to choose the best answer.

2. There are short-answer questions for which you will write phrases or sentences on the lines provided in your booklet.

Here are some important things to remember as you take this assessment:

1. Read each passage. You may look back at the reading passage as often as you want.

2. The paragraphs are numbered for all reading passages. A question about a particular paragraph will refer to the paragraph number.

3. Read each question carefully. When you write your answers, write them neatly and clearly on the lines provided. You may use sentences, phrases, paragraphs, lists, or charts to explain your ideas. Cross out or erase any part of your work you do not want to include as part of your answer.

4. When you choose a multiple-choice answer, make sure you completely fill in the circle next to the answer. Erase completely any marks that you want to change on multiple-choice items.

5. Use only a **No. 2 pencil**, not a mechanical pencil or pen, to write your answers. If you do not have a No. 2 pencil, ask your teacher to give you one.

6. You should have plenty of time to finish every question on the assessment. If you do not know the answer to a question, go on to the next question. You can come back to that question later.

7. When you reach the word **STOP** in your booklet, you have reached the end of Assessment Two. Do not go on until you are told to turn the page.

8. If you finish early, you may check your work in this session **only**.

Go on ▶

Directions: Read the story and answer the questions.

Pioneer Life and Customs
Federal Writers' Project (Works Progress Administration)

1   I guess I know about as many people in Oregon as anybody: I've lived here long enough, heaven knows. We used to have some good times back in those days of the horse and buggy, as they call 'em now. That reminds me, I guess I engineered the first automobile race in the Northwest. It was up in Dayton, Washington—and that section was of the Old Oregon country, so I'll tell about it. There was to be a Fourth of July celebration, and it struck me a race between those new-fangled machines would attract a lot of attention. It did too. We had it on the town race-track, a half-mile track, and the automobiles were of the Olds manufacture, one of the first models, high and ornate, with brass trimmings. I don't remember anything about the cylinders. Maybe there weren't any. Anyway my wife and I got in one with the owner, who was to drive, and the owner of the other machine filled his up and off we went, while the excited spectators—and they came from all over the country—yelled, "Whip her up!"... "Shove her along!"... "Take the whip to her!"... and anything they could think of to make us go faster. Such a thing as "Step on it!" or any other motor phraseology was then unknown. We responded as best we could, going faster and faster at what seemed a terrific rate, until we completed the second lap. The passengers were scared half to death. It developed when we finished, almost as a tie, that we had achieved the unbelievable speed of 18 miles an hour! (if I remember, those machines cost $1500.00). When, a few years later, Barney Olds drove his "Red Devil" Cadillac on the old Irvington race track here in Portland, the spectators gasped and shivered at his sixty miles an hour, which is no great shucks today. For that race of ours at Dayton, the women were all dolled up in yards and yards of veils. I think they had on long dusters too.

2   We used to have a lot of laughs in my early banking days. There was a camraderie at that time between officials and clerks, that don't seem to exist now. I was first in the bank at Ladd & Bush at Salem, and Salem sure was lively for some of us. I remember when the county court house was built. The architect was a young fellow named Boothby, I think he is still alive and living in Salem. He was pretty gay. When the goddess of justice that was to surmount the building was waiting to be hoisted to the top, some of the boys got hold of it one night, dressed it up in calico with a big rag baby in its arms, and pinned a notice on it to the effect that Boothby had been stepping out with the goddess of justice.

Go on ▶

1 Any one of these titles could be another title for the story. Choose the title you think best fits the story.

Early Days of Oregon

Around the Track

A Small Slice of Oregon Life

Provide **two** details from the story to support your choice.

_____

_____

_____

_____

_____

_____

_____

_____

2 Based on the story, which word best describes the Fourth of July race?

○ **A.** Innovative

○ **B.** Dull

○ **C.** Commonplace

○ **D.** Conventional

Go on ▶

3   How are the first automobile race in the story and the race in Portland a few years later in the story different?

   ○ A.   In the first race, the car drove 60 mph; in the second race, it drove twice that fast.

   ○ B.   In the first race, the car drove 60 mph; in the second race, it drove only half that fast.

   ○ C.   In the first race, 18 mph seemed like a high speed; in the second race, the speed was 60 mph.

   ○ D.   In the first race, 18 mph didn't seem like a high speed; in the second race, it did.

4   What is the author's purpose for writing the story?

   ○ **A.**   To demonstrate camaraderie between officials and clerks.

   ○ **B.**   To explain how to engineer an auto race.

   ○ **C.**   To show what life was like many years ago in the Northwest.

   ○ **D.**   To persuade the reader to celebrate car racing in the Northwest.

Go on ▶

5 Based on the information in the story, which conclusion can the reader draw about the narrator?

○ **A.** He didn't have much contact with those in his community.

○ **B.** He was disliked by many members of the community.

○ **C.** He was a well-known community member.

○ **D.** He did not live in the community for very long.

6 What does the narrator mean when he says "There was a camaraderie at that time between officials and clerks, that doesn't seem to exist now" in paragraph 2 of the selection?

○ **A.** Clerks and officials have always interacted in a friendly manner.

○ **B.** Clerks and officials used to not interact with one another, but now they do.

○ **C.** Clerks and officials didn't get along in the past, and they don't get along today.

○ **D.** Clerks and officials used to get along in a way that is not as common today.

7 What object does the author personify?

○ **A.** A car

○ **B.** A horse and buggy

○ **C.** The bank

○ **D.** The women

Go on ▶

Directions: Read the selection and answer the questions.

Eels

1   Although the eel looks like it could be some variety of underwater snake, true eels (members of the order *Anguilliformes*) are actually a type of fish. These fascinating fish can be found in waters around almost every continent in the world. There are approximately 20 different families of eels—many of which are not particularly well-known—and different species can be found either in fresh water or in salt water.

2   The most common type of eel is the moray eel. Moray eels are saltwater eels that live in tropical seas, often in coral reefs or in shallow, rocky areas of the sea. A moray eel has thick, scaleless skin, small eyes, and a wide mouth with numerous sharp teeth. Along with the skin, the inside of a moray's mouth is camouflaged; morays keep their mouths open to keep water circulating through the gills, which are located on the sides of the head behind the mouth. Most morays grow to be about one meter long, but some may grow as large as three meters in length.

3   Unlike most types of fish, moray eels do not have paired fins on the sides, and even their top, bottom, and tail fins are covered with a thick skin to protect them from injury as the eel swims among rough rocks and coral. Since they are nocturnal creatures, morays hide in holes and cracks in rock or coral during the day and emerge at night to do their hunting, which they perform primarily based on smell. Although a moray will generally not attack anything larger than itself, there are instances when a diver has been bitten after having a part of the body, especially the hands or feet, come too close to an eel's shelter.

4   Freshwater eels have scales, but the scales are usually so small and are set so deep into the skin that they are hard to see; thus, freshwater eels often appear to be scaleless. They have small heads and small paired fins on the sides of the head, though these fins are sometimes lost when the eel reaches maturity. Like moray eels, freshwater eels have wide mouths and strong teeth. Most freshwater eels grow to be between one and two meters long.

5   Freshwater eels do not actually live in fresh water their entire lives. Once a freshwater eel reaches maturity, it swims out to sea to spawn. A freshwater eel that goes out to sea to spawn never makes it back to fresh water; it dies at sea as its young drift on the ocean. When the young have grown somewhat, they swim upstream until they reach fresh water, and the cycle continues.

Go on ▶

8   Which sentence tells how moray eels and freshwater eels are similar?

○ **A.**   Freshwater eels have scales, but the scales are usually so small and are set so deep into the skin that they are hard to see; thus, freshwater eels often appear to be scaleless.

○ **B.**   Like moray eels, freshwater eels have wide mouths and strong teeth.

○ **C.**   Most freshwater eels grow to be between one and two meters long.

○ **D.**   A moray eel has thick, scaleless skin, small eyes, and a wide mouth with numerous sharp teeth.

9   In paragraph 5 of the selection, why does the author include information about the spawning cycle of freshwater eels? Include **two** details from the selection in your answer.

_____

_____

_____

_____

_____

_____

_____

_____

Go on ▶

10   After reading the selection, which generalization can the reader make about moray eels?

     ○   **A.**   They will attack any diver who is in the water near them.

     ○   **B.**   They are likely to attack a diver who comes too close to their shelters.

     ○   **C.**   They are likely to attack a diver if they are very hungry.

     ○   **D.**   There are no known instances of a moray eel attacking a diver.

11   Which sentence from the selection is an opinion?

     ○   **A.**   "The most common type of eel is the moray eel."

     ○   **B.**   "Freshwater eels do not actually live in fresh water their entire lives."

     ○   **C.**   "Although the eel looks like it could be some variety of underwater snake, true eels (members of the order *Anguilliformes*) are actually a type of fish."

     ○   **D.**   "These fascinating fish can be found in waters around almost every continent in the world."

Go on ▶

12 Which sentence best states a main theme of the selection "Eels"?

   ○ **A.** Eels are a variety of underwater snake.

   ○ **B.** Moray eels are different from most other types of fish.

   ○ **C.** The ocean contains many different types of eels and fish.

   ○ **D.** There many different species of eels found in fresh and salt water.

13 Which sentence summarizes the selection?

   ○ **A.** Eels look more like snakes than fish, but they are really a type of fish.

   ○ **B.** Most moray eels grow to be about one meter long, and freshwater eels grow to be between one and two meters long.

   ○ **C.** Freshwater eels appear to be scaleless, but they are actually covered in tiny scales.

   ○ **D.** Eels are a type of fish with an unusual physical structure, and different varieties of eels can be found in salt water and in fresh water.

Go on ▶

14 What is the meaning of the word *circulating* as it is used in paragraph 2 of the selection?

    ○ **A.** To move continuously

    ○ **B.** To move slowly

    ○ **C.** To run fast

    ○ **D.** To rely on

Go on ▶

Directions: Read the selection and answer the questions.

Annie Smith Peck: Mountaineer

1   The roster of explorers in the early history of the Americas is littered with the names of men. Few women's names make their way into popular history in this area. Although it's true that the majority of explorers were men, plenty of women achieved significant goals in this field; Annie Smith Peck was one of these women.

2   Annie Smith Peck was born in Providence, Rhode Island, in 1850. After graduating from high school, Peck enrolled at the Rhode Island Normal School, and following graduation from that school, she went on to become a teacher. Most women in the late 19th century did not attain education at a higher level than Peck had completed; however, within a few years, she decided she wanted more. Annie Peck enrolled in a program of Greek and classical languages at the University of Michigan, and graduated again in 1878—just eight years after the school began admitting women. She landed a number of college teaching positions and became a well-known public lecturer.

3   Even after these accomplishments, Peck wanted to do more, so she took up mountain climbing at age 44. She became the third woman to climb to the top of the Matterhorn (located in the Swiss Alps). Looking for a new challenge, Peck became the first person—man or woman—to scale the north peak of Mount Huascaran in Peru, a height of more than 22,000 feet. Since it was not known at the time exactly how tall Mount Huascaran and some other tall peaks were, she believed for a while that she had climbed the tallest mountain anywhere in the Americas. This turned out not to be the case, but climbing Mount Huascaran was still a major triumph. Reaching the peak took Peck half a dozen tries, and she received limited funds and had to use equipment designed for men that often didn't fit her. When she climbed Mount Huascaran in 1908, Peck was 58 years old.

4   Annie Peck continued to climb mountains until late in her life. She placed a pennant supporting women's suffrage at the top of another Peruvian summit in 1909. In 1932, Peck wrote and published a book titled *Flying over South America: Twenty Thousand Miles by Air* after taking a seven-month journey across South America by plane. She climbed her final peak in New Hampshire at age 82, less than three years before her death.

Go on▶

15 What is the meaning of the word *roster* as it is used in paragraph 1 of the selection?

    ○ **A.**   List

    ○ **B.**   Schedule

    ○ **C.**   Platform

    ○ **D.**   Celebration

16 Which sentence from the selection is an example of imagery?

    ○ **A.**   "Although it's true that the majority of explorers were men, plenty of women achieved significant goals in this field."

    ○ **B.**   "Looking for a new challenge, Peck became the first person—man or woman—to scale the north peak of Mount Huascaran in Peru, a height of more than 22,000 feet."

    ○ **C.**   "The roster of explorers in the early history of the Americas is littered with the names of men."

    ○ **D.**   "Annie Peck continued to climb mountains until late in her life."

Go on ▶

17 The selection shows that someone can overcome challenges to achieve a difficult goal. Provide **two** details from the selection that support this idea.

_____

_____

_____

_____

_____

_____

_____

_____

18 What is most likely the author's purpose for writing this selection?

○ **A.** To persuade readers to follow the same path as Annie Smith Peck and become a mountaineer.

○ **B.** To demonstrate the role of a mountaineer to the reader.

○ **C.** To describe to the reader how to become a teacher and how to climb mountains.

○ **D.** To inform readers about a mountaineer woman and her accomplishments.

Go on ▶

19 Based on the information in the selection, what assumption can the reader make about Annie Smith Peck's graduating class at the University of Michigan?

○ **A.** The majority of the class was most likely women.

○ **B.** The majority of the class was most likely men.

○ **C.** The class most likely had equal numbers of men and women.

○ **D.** There were no other students who graduated at the same time as Peck.

20 According to the selection, what happens after Annie takes a seven-month journey across South America by plane?

○ **A.** She becomes a well-known lecturer.

○ **B.** She enrolls in college.

○ **C.** She publishes a book.

○ **D.** She climbs her final peak.

Go on ➤

21 What is unique about the Mount Huascaran?

○ **A.** Mount Huascaran is the tallest mountain anywhere in the Americas.

○ **B.** Mount Huascaran is located in the Swiss Alps.

○ **C.** Mount Huascaran has a height of more than 22,000 feet.

○ **D.** Mount Huascaran has the women's suffrage pennant placed on its summit.

Go on ▶

Directions: Read the story and answer the questions.

Traveling West

1   Dear Diary,

2   Finally, we made it to California. It feels like we've been traveling the trail forever, but father says it's only been five months. It feels like years since we left Upper Independence Landing, and I know we stayed in Independence for at least 10 days before heading out on the trail.

3   The journey was difficult; there were moments when I truly believed we would never reach the end of the trail. Merrill was stricken with a severe illness about halfway through, and for some time, I was immensely afraid that we might lose him to the sickness. He recovered, however, and we continued west, thoughts of California ever increasing in our minds and hearts.

4   As we neared the end of the journey, we encountered beautiful and amazing mountains; we would soon find, though, that their beauty was overshadowed by the treacherous task of crossing them. In some areas, the rocks were prevalent, and unstable; in others, the ground was soft and the oxen would occasionally slip into the earth. We moved quite slowly, and it took us a great many days to wind through the mountains.

5   Now, we are here in California, at Fort Sutter. The land is more beautiful than I could have imagined! Brilliant orange flowers fill the landscape as I look to all sides of me. The air is as warm as the biggest campfire. I am excited about beginning our new life in the west.

6   Amelia

Go on ▶

22 Which two objects does the author compare using a simile?

○ **A.**   Mountains and rocks

○ **B.**   Flowers and landscapes

○ **C.**   Illness and California

○ **D.**   Warm air and a campfire

23 Which word could the author have used in paragraph 2 instead of *immensely*?

○ **A.**   Very

○ **B.**   Not

○ **C.**   A little

○ **D.**   Slightly

24 Which sentence best summarizes the story?

○ **A.**   Amelia's story is about her journey traveling west and her thoughts of living in California.

○ **B.**   Amelia's story is about her difficult journey traveling west, some of the hardships she endured, and then finally her arrival to a new life in California.

○ **C.**   Amelia's family's story is about their hardships during their journey to Fort Sutter in California.

○ **D.**   Amelia's story is about her five month journey from Upper Independence Landing through Independence and then eventually her arrival to a new life in California.

Go on ▶

TIMELINE OF THE CALIFORNIA TRAIL

1821 THE SANTA FE TRAIL, BEGINNING IN INDEPENDENCE, MISSOURI, AND ENDING IN SANTA FE, NEW MEXICO, IS COMPLETED.

1828 JEDEDIAH SMITH NAVIGATES THE SIERRA NEVADA—THE FIRST RECORDED ACCOUNT OF THIS EVENT. THIS CROSSING WOULD LATER BE A PART OF THE CALIFORNIA TRAIL.

1829 THE OLD SPANISH TRAIL IS BUILT BETWEEN SOUTHERN CALIFORNIA AND SANTA FE.

1841 A GROUP OF PIONEERS TRAVELING THE OREGON TRAIL DECIDE TO TAKE A DETOUR TO THE SOUTH AND END UP IN CALIFORNIA.

1841 JOHN SUTTER BUILDS A FORT IN THE AREA OF CALIFORNIA NOW KNOWN AS SACRAMENTO.

1846–1848 THE UNITED STATES ACQUIRES POSSESSION OF CALIFORNIA AND THE SOUTHWEST IN THE MEXICAN-AMERICAN WAR.

1848 GOLD IS DISCOVERED IN CALIFORNIA, LEADING TO MORE THAN 100,000 NEW IMMIGRANTS.

1850 CALIFORNIA GAINS ENOUGH POPULATION TO BE ADMITTED AS A STATE.

1862–1869 THE TRANSCONTINENTAL RAILROAD IS PROPOSED, FUNDED, AND BUILT, MAKING TRAVEL TO CALIFORNIA MUCH EASIER.

Go on ▶

25 Which statement is the most important conclusion the reader may draw from the selection?

    ○ **A.**   Very few people made the journey along the California Trail because it was too difficult.

    ○ **B.**   Although the journey along the California Trail was difficult, thousands of settlers made the trip to California.

    ○ **C.**   The California Trail was not open to settlers; only professional mountaineers like Jedediah Smith were allowed to make the journey.

    ○ **D.**   The California Trail brought many settlers to California, but not enough to help California become a state.

26 Any of these phrases might be used to identify the author's purpose for writing the selection. Choose the phrase that best describes the author's purpose for writing the selection.

To entertain

To inform

To explain

Support your choice with **two** details from the selection.

_____

_____

_____

_____

_____

_____

_____

_____

Go on ▶

27 The author of "Traveling West" states that "the journey was difficult." Provide **two** examples from "Timeline of the California Trail" that show how traveling the trail was hard work.

_____

_____

_____

_____

_____

_____

_____

Go on ▶

28 Which sentence tells how each selection's description of Fort Sutter is different?

- ○ **A.** "Traveling West" presents Fort Sutter from a personal perspective; "Timeline of the California Trail" gives a couple of facts about it.

- ○ **B.** "Traveling West" gives a couple of facts about Fort Sutter; "Timeline of the California Trail" gives the timeline of the fort's construction.

- ○ **C.** "Traveling West" presents Fort Sutter from the view of a historian; "Timeline of the California Trail" presents the fort from a personal perspective.

- ○ **D.** "Traveling West" presents Fort Sutter from the view of a famous historian; "Timeline of the California Trail" gives a couple of facts about it.

29 How are the California Trail and the Santa Fe Trail from the two selections alike?

- ○ **A.** Both end in Santa Fe, New Mexico.

- ○ **B.** Both end in Sacramento, California.

- ○ **C.** Both begin in Oregon.

- ○ **D.** Both begin in Independence, Missouri.

Go on ▶

© Englefield & Associates, Inc.

Directions: Read the selection and answer the questions.

Lacrosse

1   In many regions of the United States and Canada, more and more people are starting to play lacrosse. Although this exciting sport has gained noticeable popularity in the last half of the twentieth century, its origins date back hundreds of years earlier. In fact, missionaries who were in the Great Lakes area have records of Native Americans playing the sport as early as the 1630s.

The Origins

2   Lacrosse, as played by Native Americans, had three common forms. One, played mainly in the Southeast, required players to hold a two-and-a-half foot stick in each hand and cup the ball between them. A version common to the Great Lakes area was played with a three-foot stick with a closed pocket that was roughly the size of the ball. The final form came from the Northeast and consisted of a stick longer than three feet that ended in a crook, with webbing that formed a pocket. This last version most closely resembles the form of lacrosse played today.

3   The name lacrosse, coined by French settlers, is simply a generic term for a game played with a curved stick, known as a "crosse," and a ball. For Native Americans, however, lacrosse was more than a simple game. The basis of the sport as they played it was rooted in legend, and there was much ceremony surrounding their playing of it. As the influence of settlers worn away Native American culture, violence and betting surrounding the game increased, which inspired opposition from the government and eventually a ban on the sport around the year 1900.

Modern Lacrosse

4   As the Native American version of lacrosse was falling out of favor, many non-natives were picking up the game. At the St. Louis Olympics in 1904, lacrosse was played as an exhibition sport. This same year, a group of individuals formed a committee to establish regulations for college lacrosse and to divide colleges into northern and southern divisions. A similar association for women's lacrosse was formed in 1931 and held its first national tournament in 1933.

5   In the past 35 years, the sport has continued its rapid growth, beginning with men's lacrosse's alliance with the NCAA in 1971. Today, more than half a million athletes worldwide play lacrosse. The game is no longer played with handmade wooden sticks; lacrosse sticks today are most commonly manufactured from aluminum and plastic. The men's version of the sport has changed quite a bit from the native game, but the women's version still bears some resemblance to the game Native Americans played for hundreds of years.

Go on ▶

30 Which sentence from the selection is an opinion?

   ○ **A.** "A version common to the Great Lakes area was played with a three-foot stick with a closed pocket that was roughly the size of the ball."

   ○ **B.** "At the St. Louis Olympics in 1904, lacrosse was played as an exhibition sport."

   ○ **C.** "Although this exciting sport has gained noticeable popularity in the last half of the twentieth century, its origins date back hundreds of years earlier."

   ○ **D.** "In many regions of the United States and Canada, more and more people are starting to play lacrosse."

31 What is the purpose of the subheadings in the selection?

   ○ **A.** To give readers a basic understanding of the history of lacrosse before they read the more detailed version in the selection.

   ○ **B.** To show readers that part of the selection deals with the origins of lacrosse and part of it deals with the modern version of the game.

   ○ **C.** To show readers the increase in the number of lacrosse players in the past 50 years.

   ○ **D.** To let readers know what the entire selection is about.

32 Based on the information in the selection, what assumption can the reader make about the popularity of lacrosse in the future?

   ○ **A.** Lacrosse will most likely continue to increase in popularity, since its popularity is relatively recent.

   ○ **B.** Lacrosse's popularity will decrease, because people who know the sport's history will not want to play it.

   ○ **C.** Lacrosse will not get any more popular than it is now, since it has been at the same popularity level for decades.

   ○ **D.** Lacrosse will quickly become less popular, since it has been picked up as both a men's and women's college sport.

Go on ▶

33 According to the section **Modern Lacrosse**, which statement is true?

   ○ **A.**   In 1904, a committee was formed to establish rules for college lacrosse.

   ○ **B.**   Only Native Americans played lacrosse in the 1930s.

   ○ **C.**   French settlers coined the term lacrosse.

   ○ **D.**   Modern lacrosse players still use handmade wooden sticks.

Go on ▶

34 Which statement is the most important conclusion the reader may draw from the selection?

    ○ **A.** Things that seem to be recent trends often have beginnings dating much farther back than people realize.

    ○ **B.** A sport cannot become popular with people until it has been in the Olympics.

    ○ **C.** The popularity of trendy sports usually does not last for very long.

    ○ **D.** Most of the famous sports in North America come from the Great Lakes area.

35 What is the meaning of the word *exhibition* as it is used in paragraph 4 of the selection?

    ○ **A.** Competition

    ○ **B.** Fight

    ○ **C.** Ban

    ○ **D.** Demonstration

STOP

Mathematics

Introduction

In the Mathematics Assessment of the Measurements of Student Progress (MSP), you will be asked questions to test the knowledge you have learned so far in school. These questions are based on the mathematical skills you have been taught in school through seventh grade. The questions you answer are not meant to confuse or trick you but are written so you have the best opportunity to show what you know about mathematics.

The *Show What You Know® on the MSP for Grade 7, Student Workbook* includes a Mathematics Tutorial that will help you practice your test-taking skills. Following the Mathematics Tutorial is a full-length Mathematics Assessment. Both the Mathematics Tutorial and the Mathematics Assessment have been created to model the Grade 7 Measurements of Student Progress for Mathematics.

About the Mathematics MSP

The Grade 7 Mathematics Assessment will test Content (numbers, operations, algebra, geometry/measurement, data/statistics/probability) as well as Process (reasoning, problem solving, and communication). The Mathematics Assessment is given in one session.

For the Mathematics Assessment there are three different types of questions: multiple choice, completion items, and short answer. Dictionaries, thesauruses, and scratch paper are not allowed on the Mathematics Assessment.

Scoring

On the MSP for Grade 7 Mathematics Assessment, each multiple-choice item is worth one point. Short-answer items will be scored on a scale of zero to two points. Completion items are worth one point each. The scoring criteria will focus on the understanding of mathematical ideas, information, and solutions, and will disregard conventions of writing (complete sentences, usage/grammar, spelling, capitals, punctuation, and paragraphing), as long as the wording of the response does not interfere with the mathematical communication.

Item and Point Totals

Type	Number of Items	Total Possible Points
Multiple Choice	25	25
Completion Items	5	5
Short Answer	5	10
Total	35	40

Glossary

addend: Numbers added together to give a sum. For example, 2 + 7 = 9. The numbers 2 and 7 are addends.

addition: An operation joining two or more sets where the result is the whole.

a.m.: The hours from midnight to noon; from Latin words *ante meridiem* meaning "before noon."

analyze: To break down information into parts so that it may be more easily understood.

angle: A figure formed by two rays that meet at the same end point called a vertex. Angles can be obtuse, acute, right, or straight.

area: The number of square units needed to cover a region. The most common abbreviation for area is *A*.

Associative Property of Addition: The grouping of addends can be changed and the sum will be the same. Example: (3 + 1) + 2 = 6; 3 + (1 + 2) = 6.

Associative Property of Multiplication: The grouping of factors can be changed and the product will be the same. Example: (3 x 2) x 4 = 24; 3 x (2 x 4) = 24.

attribute: A characteristic or distinctive feature.

average: A number found by adding two or more quantities together and then dividing the sum by the number of quantities. For example, in the set {9, 5, 3}, the average is 6: 9 + 5 + 4 = 18; 18 ÷ 3 = 6. *See mean.*

axes: Plural of axis. Perpendicular lines used as reference lines in a coordinate system or graph; traditionally, the horizontal axis (*x*-axis) represents the independent variable and the vertical axis (*y*-axis) represents the dependent variable.

bar graph: A graph using bars to show data.

capacity: The amount an object holds when filled.

chart: A way to show information, such as in a graph or table.

circle: A closed, curved line made up of points that are all the same distance from a point inside called the center. Example: A circle with center point *P* is shown below.

circle graph: Sometimes called a pie chart; a way of representing data that shows the fractional part or percentage of an overall set as an appropriately sized wedge of a circle. Example:

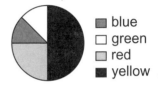

■ blue
□ green
▨ red
■ yellow

circumference: The boundary line or perimeter of a circle; also, the length of the perimeter of a circle. Example:

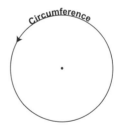

Commutative Property of Addition: Numbers can be added in any order and the sum will be the same. Example: 3 + 4 = 4 + 3.

Commutative Property of Multiplication: Numbers can be multiplied in any order and the product will be the same. Example: 3 x 6 = 6 x 3.

compare: To look for similarities and differences. For example, is one number greater than, less than, or equal to another number?

conclusion: A statement that follows logically from other facts.

Glossary

cone: A solid figure with a circle as its base and a curved surface that meets at a point.

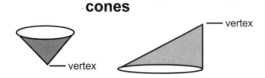

congruent figures: Figures that have the same shape and size.

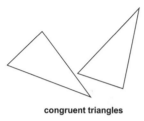

congruent triangles

cube: A solid figure with six faces that are congruent (equal) squares.

cylinder: A solid figure with two circular bases that are congruent (equal) and parallel to each other connected by a curved lateral surface.

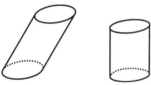

data: Information that is collected.

decimal number: A number expressed in base 10, such as 39.356, where each digit's value is determined by multiplying it by some power of 10.

denominator: The bottom number in a fraction.

diagram: A drawing that represents a mathematical situation.

difference: The answer when subtracting two numbers.

distance: The amount of space between two points.

dividend: A number in a division problem that is divided. Dividend ÷ divisor = quotient. Example: In 15 ÷ 3 = 5, 15 is the dividend.

$$\text{divisor}\overline{)\text{dividend}}^{\text{quotient}} \qquad 3\overline{)15}^{\,5}$$

divisible: Can be divided by another number without leaving a remainder. Example: 12 is divisible by 3 because 12 ÷ 3 is an integer, namely 4.

division: An operation that tells how many equal groups there are or how many are in each group.

divisor: The number by which another number is divided. Example: In 15 ÷ 3 = 5, 3 is the divisor.

$$\text{divisor}\overline{)\text{dividend}}^{\text{quotient}} \qquad 3\overline{)15}^{\,5}$$

edge: The line segment where two faces of a solid figure meet.

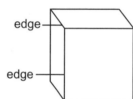

equality: Two or more sets of values that are equal.

equation: A number sentence that says two expressions are equal (=). Example: 4 + 8 = 6 + 6.

equivalent fractions: Two fractions with equal values.

estimate: To find an approximate value or measurement of something without exact calculation.

even number: A whole number that has a 0, 2, 4, 6, or 8 in the ones place. A number that is a multiple of 2. Examples: 0, 4, and 678 are even numbers.

expanded form: A number written as the sum of the values of its digits. Example: 546 = 500 + 40 + 6.

Glossary

expression: A combination of variables, numbers, and symbols that represent a mathematical relationship.

face: The sides of a solid figure. For example, a cube has six faces that are all squares. The pyramid below has five faces—four triangles and one square.

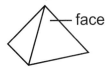

fact family: A group of related facts using the same numbers. Example: 5 + 8 = 13; 13 − 8 = 5.

factor: One of two or more numbers that are multiplied together to give a product. Example: In 3 x 4 = 12, 3 and 4 are factors of 12.

figure: A geometric figure is a set of points and/or lines in 2 or 3 dimensions.

flip (reflection): The change in a position of a figure that is the result of picking it up and turning it over.
Example: Reversing a "b" to a "d."
Tipping a "p" to a "b" or a "b" to a "p" as shown below:

fraction: A symbol, such as $\frac{2}{8}$ or $\frac{5}{3}$, used to name a part of a whole, a part of a set, or a location on the number line. Examples:

$$\frac{\text{numerator}}{\text{denominator}} = \frac{\text{dividend}}{\text{divisor}}$$

$$\frac{\text{\# of parts under consideration}}{\text{\# of parts in a set}}$$

function machine: Applies a function rule to a set of numbers, which determines a corresponding set of numbers.
Example: Input 9 → Rule x 7 → Output 63. If you apply the function rule "multiply by 7" to the values 5, 7, and 9, the corresponding values are:
$$5 \rightarrow 35$$
$$7 \rightarrow 49$$
$$9 \rightarrow 63$$

graph: A "picture" showing how certain facts are related to each other or how they compare to one another. Some examples of types of graphs are line graphs, pie charts, bar graphs, scatterplots, and pictographs.

grid: A pattern of regularly spaced horizontal and vertical lines on a plane that can be used to locate points and graph equations.

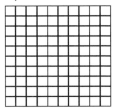

hexagon: A six-sided polygon. The total measure of the angles within a hexagon is 720°.

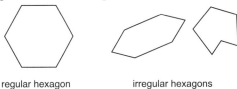

regular hexagon   irregular hexagons

impossible event: An event that can never happen.

integer: Any number, positive or negative, that is a whole number distance away from zero on a number line, in addition to zero. Specifically, an integer is any number in the set {. . .-3,-2,-1, 0, 1, 2, 3. . .}. Examples of integers include: 1, 5, 273, -2, -35, and -1,375.

intersecting lines: Lines that cross at a point. Examples:

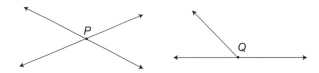

Glossary

isosceles triangle: A triangle with at least two sides the same length.

justify: To prove or show to be true or valid using logic and/or evidence.

key: An explanation of what each symbol represents in a pictograph.

kilometer (km): A metric unit of length: 1 kilometer = 1,000 meters.

line: A straight path of points that goes on forever in both directions.

line graph: A graph that uses a line or a curve to show how data changes over time.

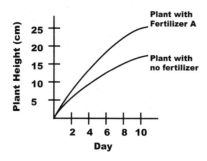

line of symmetry: A line on which a figure can be folded into two parts so that the parts match exactly.

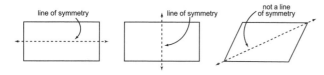

liter (L): A metric unit of capacity: 1 liter = 1,000 milliliters.

mass: The amount of matter an object has.

mean: Also called arithmetic average. A number found by adding two or more quantities together, and then dividing the sum by the number of quantities. For example, in the set {9, 5, 3} the mean is 6: 9 + 5 + 4 = 18; 18 ÷ 3 = 6. *See average.*

median: The middle number when numbers are put in order from least to greatest or from greatest to least. For example, in the set of numbers 6, 7, 8, 9, 10, the number 8 is the median (middle) number.

meter (m): A metric unit of length: 1 meter = 100 centimeters.

method: A systematic way of accomplishing a task.

mixed number: A number consisting of a whole number and a fraction.
Example: $6\frac{2}{3}$.

mode: The number or numbers that occur most often in a set of data. Example: The mode of {1, 3, 4, 5, 5, 7, 9} is 5.

multiple: A product of a number and any other whole number. Examples: {2, 4, 6, 8, 10, 12,…} are multiples of 2.

multiplication: An operation on two numbers that tells how many in all. The first number is the number of sets and the second number tells how many in each set.

number line: A line that shows numbers in order using a scale. Equal intervals are marked and usually labeled on the number line.

number sentence: An expression of a relationship between quantities as an equation or an inequality. Examples: 7 + 7 = 8 + 6; 13 < 92; 56 + 4 > 59.

numerator: The top number in a fraction.

octagon: An eight-sided polygon. The total measure of the angles within an octagon is 1080°.

regular   irregular
octagon   octagons

odd number: A whole number that has 1, 3, 5, 7, or 9 in the ones place. An odd number is not divisible by 2. Examples: The numbers 53 and 701 are odd numbers.

operation: A mathematical process that combines numbers; basic operations of arithmetic include addition, subtraction, multiplication, and division.

order: To arrange numbers from the least to greatest or from the greatest to least.

Glossary

ordered pair: Two numbers inside a set of parentheses separated by a comma that are used to name a point on a coordinate grid.

parallel lines: Lines in the same plane that never intersect.

parallelogram: A quadrilateral in which opposite sides are parallel.

pattern: An arrangement of numbers, pictures, etc., in an organized and predictable way. Examples: 3, 6, 9, 12, or ® 0 ® 0 ® 0.

pentagon: A five-sided polygon. The total measure of the angles within a pentagon is 540°.

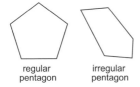

regular
pentagon

irregular
pentagon

perimeter: The distance around a figure.

perpendicular lines: Two lines that intersect to form a right angle (90 degrees).

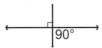

90°

pictograph: A graph that uses pictures or symbols to represent similar data. The value of each picture is interpreted by a "key" or "legend."

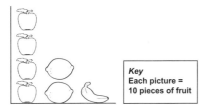

Key
Each picture =
10 pieces of fruit

place value: The value given to the place a digit has in a number.
Example: In the number 135, the 1 is in the hundreds place so it represents 100 (1 x 100), the 3 is in the tens place so it represents 30 (3 x 10), and the 5 is in the ones place so it represents 5 (5 x 1).

p.m.: The hours from noon to midnight; from the Latin words *post meridiem* meaning "after noon."

point: An exact position often marked by a dot.

polygon: A closed figure made up of straight line segments.

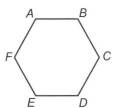

ABCDEF is a polygon.

possible event: An event that might or might not happen.

predict: To tell what you believe may happen in the future.

prediction: A description of what may happen before it happens.

probability: The likelihood that something will happen.

product: The answer to a multiplication problem. Example: In 3 x 4 = 12, 12 is the product.

pyramid: A solid figure in which the base is a polygon and faces are triangles with a common point called a vertex.

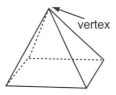

vertex

quadrilateral: A four-sided polygon. Rectangles, squares, parallelograms, rhombi, and trapezoids are all quadrilaterals. The total measure of the angles within a quadrilateral is 360°. Example: *ABCD* is a quadrilateral.

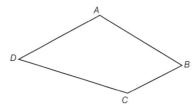

questionnaire: A set of questions for a survey.

Glossary

quotient: The answer in a division problem. Dividend ÷ divisor = quotient. Example: In 15 ÷ 3 = 5, 5 is the quotient.

range: The difference between the least number and the greatest number in a data set. For example, in the set {4, 7, 10, 12, 36, 7, 2}, the range is 34; the greatest number (36) minus the least number (2): (36 − 2 = 34).

rectangle: A quadrilateral with four right angles. A square is one example of a rectangle.

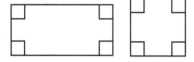

reflection: The change in the position of a figure that is the result of picking it up and turning it over. *See flip.*

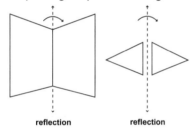

reflection   reflection

remainder: The number that is left over after dividing. Example: In 31 ÷ 7 = 4 R 3, the 3 is the remainder.

represent: To present clearly; describe; show.

rhombus: A quadrilateral with opposite sides parallel and all sides the same length. A square is one kind of rhombus.

right angle: An angle that forms a square corner and measures 90 degrees.

right triangle: A triangle having one right angle. *See angle and triangle.*

rounding: Replacing an exact number with a number that tells about how much or how many to the nearest ten, hundred, thousand, and so on. Example: 52 rounded to the nearest 10 is 50.

rule: A procedure; a prescribed method; a way of describing the relationship between two sets of numbers. Example: In the following data, the rule is to add 3:

Input	Output
3	6
5	8
9	12

ruler: A straight-edged instrument used for measuring the lengths of objects. A ruler usually measures smaller units of length, such as inches or centimeters.

scale: The numbers that show the size of the units used on a graph.

sequence: A set of numbers arranged in a special order or pattern.

set: A group made up of numbers, figures, or parts.

side: A line segment connected to other segments to form the boundary of a polygon.

similar: A description for figures that have the same shape.

slide (translation): The change in the position of a figure that moves up, down, or sideways. Example: scooting a book on a table.

solids: Figures in three dimensions.

solve: To find the solution to an equation or problem; finding the values of unknown variables that will make a true mathematical statement.

sphere: A solid figure in the shape of a ball. Example: a basketball is a sphere.

Glossary

square: A rectangle with congruent (equal) sides. *See rectangle.*

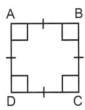

square number: The product of a number multiplied by itself. Example: 49 is a square number (7 x 7 = 49).

square unit: A square with sides 1 unit long, used to measure area.

standard form: A way to write a number showing only its digits. Example: 2,389.

standard units of measure: Units of measure commonly used; generally classified in the U.S. as the customary system or the metric system:

Customary System:
  Length
  1 foot (ft) = 12 inches (in)
  1 yard (yd) = 3 feet or 36 inches
  1 mile (mi) = 1,760 yards or 5,280 feet

  Weight
  16 ounces (oz) = 1 pound (lb)
  2,000 pounds = 1 ton (t)

  Capacity
  1 pint (pt) = 2 cups (c)
  1 quart (qt) = 2 pints
  1 gallon (gal) = 4 quarts

Metric System:
  Length
  1 centimeter (cm) = 10 millimeters (mm)
  1 decimeter (dm) = 10 centimeters
  1 meter (m) = 100 centimeters
  1 kilometer (km) = 1,000 meters

  Weight
  1,000 milligrams (mg) = 1 gram (g)
  1,000 grams (g) = 1 kilogram (kg)
  1,000 kilograms (kg) = 1 tonne (metric ton)

  Capacity
  1 liter (l) = 1,000 milliliters (ml)

strategy: A plan used in problem solving, such as looking for a pattern, drawing a diagram, working backward, etc.

subtraction: The operation that finds the difference between two numbers.

sum: The answer when adding two or more addends. Addend + Addend = Sum.

summary: A series of statements containing evidence, facts, and/or procedures that support a result.

survey: A way to collect data by asking a certain number of people the same question and recording their answers.

symmetry: A figure has line symmetry if it can be folded along a line so that both parts match exactly. A figure has radial or rotational symmetry if, after a rotation of less than 360º, it is indistinguishable from its former image.

Z unrotated   Z rotated 90º   Z rotated 180º

The letter Z has 180º radial or rotational symmetry.

table: A method of displaying data in rows and columns.

temperature: A measure of hot or cold in degrees.

translation (slide): A change in the position of a figure that moves it up, down, or sideways.

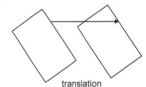

translation

Glossary

triangle: A polygon with three sides. The sum of the angles of a triangle is always equal to 180º.

turn: The change in the position of a figure that moves it around a point. Also called a rotation. Example: The hands of a clock turn around the center of the clock in a clockwise direction.

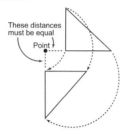

unlikely event: An event that probably will not happen.

vertex: The point where two rays meet to form an angle or where the sides of a polygon meet, or the point where 3 or more edges meet in a solid figure.

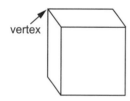

whole number: An integer in the set {0, 1, 2, 3 . . .}. In other words, a whole number is any number used when counting in addition to zero.

word forms: The number written in words. Examples: 546 is "five hundred forty-six."

Examples of Common Two-Dimensional Geometric Shapes

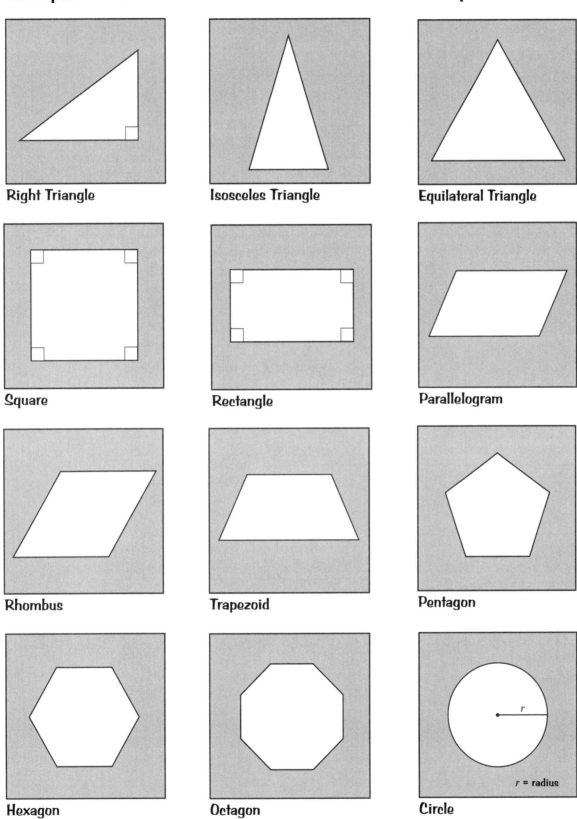

Right Triangle   **Isosceles Triangle**   **Equilateral Triangle**

Square   **Rectangle**   **Parallelogram**

Rhombus   **Trapezoid**   **Pentagon**

Hexagon   **Octagon**   **Circle**

r = radius

Examples of How Lines Interact

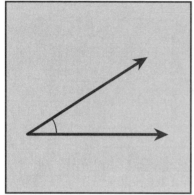

Acute Angle

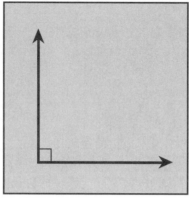

Right Angle

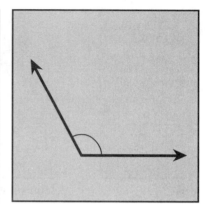

Obtuse Angle

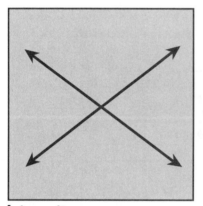

Intersecting

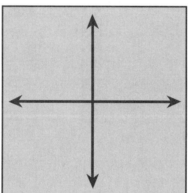

Perpendicular

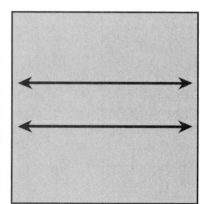

Parallel

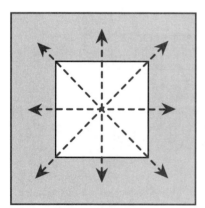

Lines of Symmetry

Examples of Common Types of Graphs

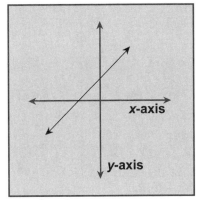

Line Graph

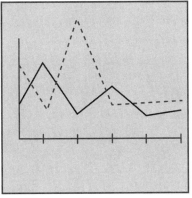

Double Line Graph

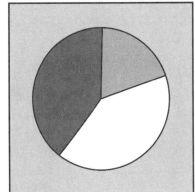

Pie Chart

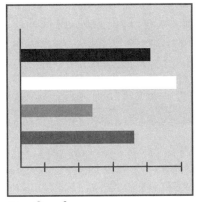

Bar Graph

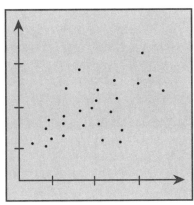

Scatterplot

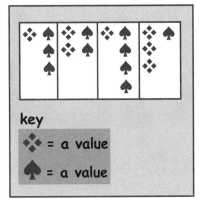

Pictograph

Examples of Common Three-Dimensional Objects

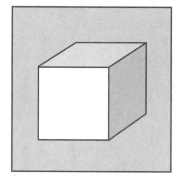

Cube

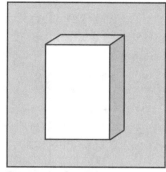

Rectangular Prism

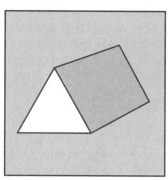

Triangular Prism

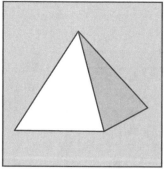

Pyramid

Cylinder

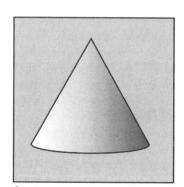

Cone

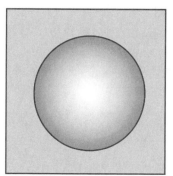

Sphere

Examples of Object Movement

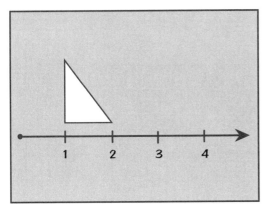
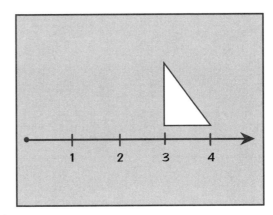

Translation

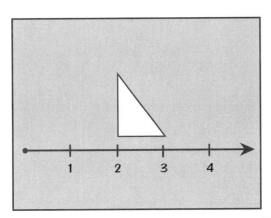
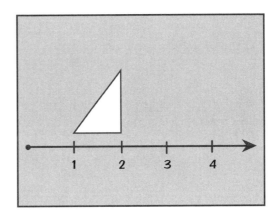

Reflection

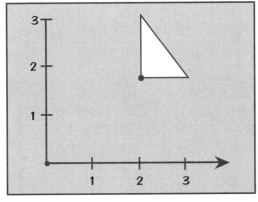
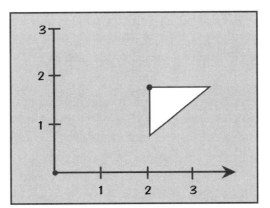

Rotation

This page left intentionally blank.

 © Englefield & Associates, Inc.

Mathematics Tutorial

The Mathematics Tutorial is made up of multiple-choice questions, completion items, and short-answer questions. These questions show you how the skills you have learned in Mathematics class may be tested on the Mathematics MSP. The questions also give you a chance to practice your skills. If you have trouble with an area, talk with a parent or teacher.

Read each question carefully. If you do not know an answer, you may skip the question and come back to it later.

When you finish, check your answers.

Directions for Mathematics Tutorial

Today you will take the Mathematics Measurements of Student Progress Tutorial.

Directions to the Student

There are several different types of questions on this tutorial:

1. Some questions will ask you to choose the best answer from among four answer choices. These items are worth one point.

2. Some questions will ask you to write or draw an answer neatly and clearly **inside** an answer box.

    *   Some of these questions are short. They may ask you to write a short answer, such as a single number or one or two words. These items are worth one point.

    *   Others ask for more details (graphs, tables, written summaries). They may ask you to write an answer, to show how you got your answer using words, numbers, or pictures, or show the steps you used to solve the problem. These questions also provide you with more room for your answer. These items are worth two points.

Here are some important things to remember as you take this tutorial:

1. Read each question carefully and think about the answer.

2. When you choose a multiple-choice answer, make sure you completely fill in the circle next to the answer. Erase completely any marks that you want to change on multiple-choice items.

3. When an answer box is provided, write your answer neatly and clearly **inside** the box and show all your work. Cross out any work you do not want as part of your answer. **Do not use scratch paper.**

4. Use only a **No. 2 pencil**, not a mechanical pencil or pen, to write your answers. If you do not have a No. 2 pencil, ask your teacher to give you one.

5. You should have plenty of time to finish every question on the tutorial. If you do not know the answer to a question, go on to the next question. You can come back to that question later.

6. When you reach the word **STOP** in your booklet, you have reached the end of the Tutorial. Do **not** go on until you are told to turn the page.

7. If you finish early, you may check your work in this session **only**.

Go on ▶

Sample Questions

To help you understand how to answer the test questions, look at the sample test questions below. They are included to show you what the questions in the test are like and how to mark or write your answers.

Multiple-Choice Sample Question

For this type of question you will select the answer and fill in the circle next to it.

1   A room is in the shape of a square with an area of 81 square feet. How many feet of crown moulding would be needed to frame the ceiling?

   ○ **A.**   12

   ○ **B.**   24

   ○ **C.**   48

   ● **D.**   36

For this sample question, the correct answer is **D**; therefore, the circle next to **D** is filled in.

Completion Item Sample Question

For this type of question you will provide a short answer such as a single number or one or two words.

2   A box of 48 chocolates has $\frac{2}{8}$ with nuts and 50% cream filled.

How many chocolates in the box are caramel, if there are only 3 kinds of chocolates in the box?

• Write how many chocolates are caramel.

> **How many chocolates in the box are caramel?** *12*

Go on ▸

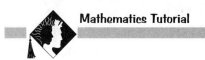

Short-Answer Sample Question

For this type of question you will write and explain your answer using words, numbers, or pictures.

3 Brian, Rob, Jim, Steve, and Pete play in a one-on-one basketball tournament. Each of them plays one game with each of the others.

How many games will be played in all?

Show or explain your work using words, numbers, and/or pictures.

_10_ games will be played in all.

Brian   Rob   Jim   Steve   Pete
  & Rob   & Jim   & Steve   & Pete
  & Jim   & Steve   & Pete
  & Steve   & Pete
  & Pete

Go on ▶

1 Which of the following numbers is the **greatest**?

- ○ **A.** $\frac{190}{10}$
- ○ **B.** 20%
- ○ **C.** 2.2×10^1
- ○ **D.** $\frac{6}{150}$

2 Which of the following number lines shows the addition of 5 and -8?

- ○ **A.**
- ○ **B.**
- ○ **C.**
- ○ **D.**

Go on ▶

3 Which of these operations results in the **lowest** value?

- ○ **A.** $\frac{1}{2} + \frac{3}{4}$

- ○ **B.** $\frac{1}{2} - \frac{3}{4}$

- ○ **C.** $\frac{1}{2} \times \frac{3}{4}$

- ○ **D.** $\frac{1}{2} \div \frac{3}{4}$

4 Which of the following best describes the **absolute value** of a number?

- ○ **A.** The absolute value is the final answer in a multi-step problem.

- ○ **B.** The absolute value is an estimate based on known data.

- ○ **C.** The absolute value is the sum of a number and all its factors.

- ○ **D.** The absolute value is the distance of a number from zero on a number line.

Go on ▶

© Englefield & Associates, Inc.

5   Solve the equation below for x.

$$3 + 6x = 21$$

- ○ **A.**   3.0
- ○ **B.**   3.5
- ○ **C.**   4.0
- ○ **D.**   4.5

6   The Upstart Communications Company offers customers a special long distance calling rate that includes a $0.25 connection fee applied to each long distance call plus a $0.10 per minute charge.

Which equation could be used to find c, the overall cost of the call, where m represents the number of minutes of the call?

- ○ **A.** $c = \$0.35m$
- ○ **B.** $c = \$0.25m + \$0.10$
- ○ **C.** $c = \$0.25 + \$0.10m$
- ○ **D.** $c = \$0.25m + \$0.10m$

Go on ➤

7   Louisa works as a clown in a circus. When she started working, she earned $12,000 per year, but was told she would receive a raise of 5% of her yearly salary each year.

If this is the third year Louisa has worked in the circus, what is her yearly salary for this year?

○ **A.** $12,600

○ **B.** $13,200

○ **C.** $13,230

○ **D.** $13,890

Go on▶

8   Which of these drawings shows the product of $\frac{2}{3}$ and $\frac{5}{6}$?

○ **A.**

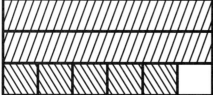

○ **B.**

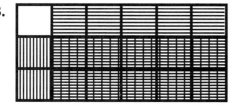

○ **C.**

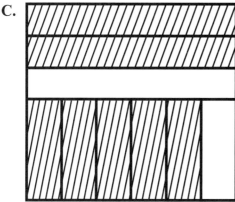

○ **D.**

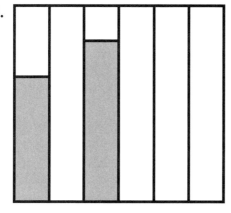

Go on ▶

9   Manny is trying maintain a consistent architectural look for his guesthouse. The height of a planned guesthouse must maintain a 4 to 7 ratio with the height of the larger main house. The main house has been designed at a height of 28 feet.

How tall will Manny's guesthouse need to be?

• Write how many feet the guesthouse will need to be.

Manny's guesthouse will need to be _____ feet.

Go on ▶

10 Which of the following right triangles is similar to a right triangle with sides 7, 24, and 25?

- ○ **A.** 21, 72, 75
- ○ **B.** 27, 96, 100
- ○ **C.** 35, 116, 125
- ○ **D.** 10, 30, 40

Go on▶

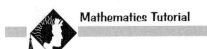
11 Tom is building a scale model of a tall ship. Using a scale of 2 inches equals 15 feet, Tom's model is 27.3 inches long.

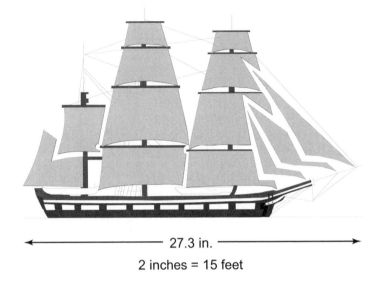

27.3 in.

2 inches = 15 feet

Determine the length of the real ship, rounded to the nearest foot. Show or describe all the steps you use to find the length of the ship.

The length of the real ship is about _____ **feet.**

Go on ▶

12 The equation, $c = \$0.75p$, lets consumers calculate the cost (c) of any number of pounds (p) of potatoes.

What amount of money completes the table below?

Cost of Potatoes

Pounds	1	3	5	7	9
$	0.75	2.25	3.75	5.25	?

The cost of **9** pounds of potatoes is $_____.

Go on ▶

13 This graph shows the amount of money in Hector's savings account and indicates how his balance grows as he makes regular deposits.

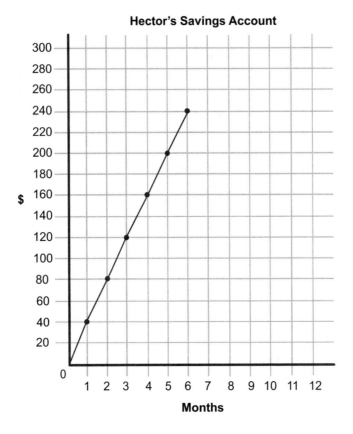

- Tell how much money Hector will have saved after one year.

- Give the slope of the line in the graph.

Go on ▶

How much money will Hector have saved after one

year?_____

What is the slope of the line in the graph?_____

Go on ▶

14   At a garage sale, Maria found a box of used CDs priced at 8 for $20.

What is the unit rate of these CDs?

   ○ **A.** $2.50

   ○ **B.** $8

   ○ **C.** $20

   ○ **D.** $160

Go on ▶

15 At Abie's CD shop you can buy CDs for $9.95; however, when you purchase more than
5 CDs, the cost of the additional CDs is reduced to only $7.50. In other words, while the first
5 CDs cost $9.95 each, the cost of the 6th or 7th CD is only $7.50.

In the space provided, tell whether or not the relationship between the number of CDs and
the cost of those CDs is proportional. Explain your reasoning.

Go on ▶

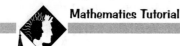

16 Manuel has measured his stride at almost exactly one yard per step.

About how many steps will he take during a 7-mile hike?

○ **A.** 251.4 steps

○ **B.** 754.2 steps

○ **C.** 12,320 steps

○ **D.** 36,960 steps

17 Grandma Wolf's chicken casserole recipe calls for half of a can of cream of chicken soup. The cylindrical can of soup has a height of 5 inches and a radius of $1\frac{1}{2}$ inches.

Using the formula for the volume of a cylinder ($v = \pi r^2 h$) calculate the **volume** of the amount of soup Grandma Wolf uses. Explain your answer.

The volume of the amount of soup

Grandma Wolf uses is _____.

Go on▶

18 Dianne has a model of a pyramid like the ones in Egypt. Her model has a square base with 8-inch sides and a height of 7.5 inches.

     • Sketch and label the pyramid

     • Then calculate the **volume** of the pyramid.

Show your work using words, numbers, and/or pictures.

                                      The volume of the pyramid is _____.

Go on ▶

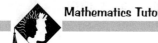

19 A small circular parachute has a radius of 20 feet. The larger model has a radius that is 40% bigger.

Which of the following best explains why the area of the larger parachute is not 40% larger than the smaller parachute?

○ **A.** The radius is not used for computing the area.

○ **B.** Since the radius is squared in the area formula, the 40% increase in radius size leads to a 96% increase in area.

○ **C.** Since the radius is by definition $\frac{1}{2}$ that of the diameter, it must be doubled before it can be used in place of the diameter in area computations.

○ **D.** This can be explained by the formula for the area of a circle and the tendency people have to round pi (π) to 3.14, instead of using a precise value.

Go on ▶

20 Ben has built a toy chest for his little brother Sam. He is now ready to paint it and plans to paint every surface, both inside and out.

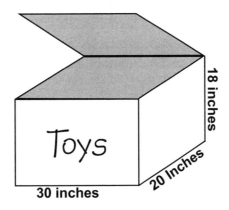

18 inches

Toys

30 inches

20 Inches

What is the **area** of the chest that Ben intends to paint?

Show your work using words, numbers, and/or pictures.

The area of the chest that Ben intends to paint is _____.

Go on ▶

21   Julio is flipping a coin and wants to keep track of the results.

• Create a tree diagram that shows all the possible results of flipping a coin 4 times in a row.

Go on ▶

22 Fatima flips a coin 4 times.

What is the **probability** that she will see at least one head?

○ **A.** $\frac{1}{2}$

○ **B.** $\frac{3}{4}$

○ **C.** $\frac{7}{8}$

○ **D.** $\frac{15}{16}$

23 Mrs. Wilshire's science class was observing ladybugs. They collected 11 ladybugs and counted the number of spots each ladybug had. They recorded this information in the graph below.

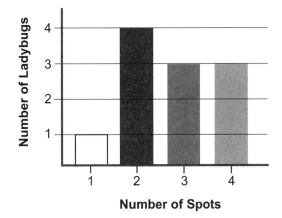

According to the data recorded in the graph, which of the following values will be the **lowest** for this data?

○ **A.** Mean

○ **B.** Median

○ **C.** Mode

○ **D.** Range

Go on ▶

24 The table below shows the daily maximum temperature for each day in August 2006 at Denver International Airport.

Daily Maximum Temperature—Denver International Airport—August 2006																															
Date	1	2	3	4	5	6	7	8	9	10	11	12	13	14	15	16	17	18	19	20	21	22	23	24	25	26	27	28	29	30	31
Max Temp °F	86	83	84	94	88	83	87	95	96	95	95	91	84	85	91	89	93	81	78	89	85	94	95	92	80	73	75	78	83	93	89

Source: National Oceanic and Atmospheric Administration; http://www.weather.gov/climate/index.php?wfo=bou

The stem-and-leaf plot below is missing four values. It is supposed to be a summary of the daily maximum temperature data from the table above.

Complete the stem-and-leaf plot by filling in the missing data.

Daily Max Temp °F – Denver International Airport – August 2006	
9	6 5 5 5 5 4 4 3 3 2 1 1
8	9 9 9 8 7 6 5 5 4 4 3 3 3 1 0

Go on ▶

Copying is Prohibited
© Englefield & Associates, Inc.

25 The table below lists the six largest countries in the world in terms of area.

Largest Countries in Square Miles, 2004

1	Russia	6,592,735
2	Canada	3,855,081
3	United States	3,717,792
4	China	3,705,386
5	Brazil	3,286,470
6	Australia	2,967,893

Source: www.infoplease.com

Which graph **best** represents the data in the table?

Describe your reason why you might choose one graph over the other.

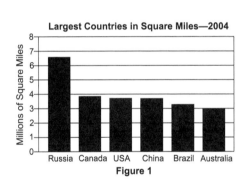

Figure 1

Largest Countries in Millions of Square Miles—2004

Figure 2

Largest Countries in Square Miles - 2004

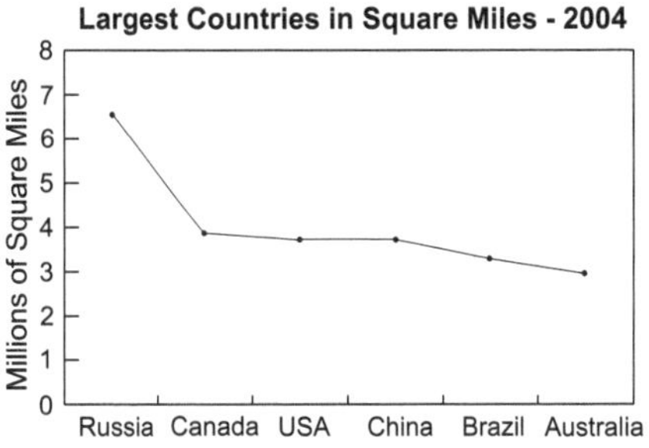

Figure 3

Which graph best represents the data in the table? Figure_____

Go on ▶

26 Consuela used a grid to map out some of her favorite places in town.

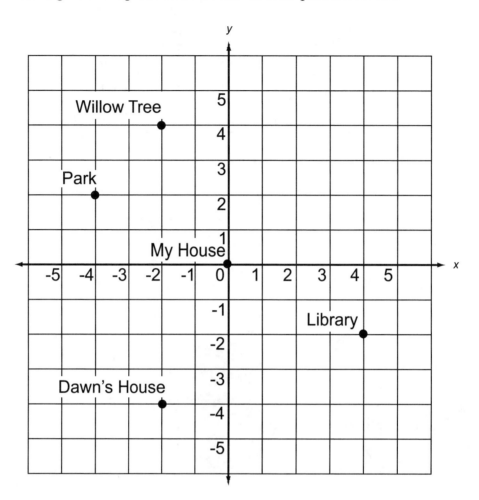

What is located at the point (–2, 4)?

○ **A.** Park

○ **B.** Library

○ **C.** Willow tree

○ **D.** Dawn's house

Go on ▶

27 What is the correct way to factor the number 400 down to prime factors?

○ **A.** 4×100

○ **B.** $2^2 \times 10^2$

○ **C.** $2^4 \times 5^2$

○ **D.** $2 \times 8 \times 5^2$

28 Laurie is driving to visit her grandmother. She began her trip at 8:00 am. During the morning part of her drive she averaged 65 mph for 4 hours. After that 4 hour period she stopped for lunch. When she finished lunch she began driving at 60 mph and covered 180 miles during the afternoon.

For which of these questions is there not enough information provided?

○ **A.**   At what time will Laurie arrive at her grandmothers?

○ **B.**   How far did Laurie drive during the morning?

○ **C.**   How many miles did she drive altogether?

○ **D.**   How many hours did she spend driving in the afternoon?

Go on ▶

29 The table below lists some interesting geography facts about Earth.

Earth Geography Facts

Age (Approximate)	4.55 billion years
Total Area:	196.940 milllion square miles
Land Area:	57.506 million square miles
Water Area:	139.434 million square miles
Terrain: Highest Land Elevation: Mt. Everest	29,035 feet
Lowest Land Elevation: Dead Sea	− 1,349 feet below sea level
Greatest Ocean Depth: Mariana Trench	− 35,840 feet below sea level
Land Use: Arable Land (Farmable)	13.31%

*The World Factbook, 2006; https://www.cia.gov/cia/publications/factbook/geos/xx.html

List two facts from the table above that you need in order to calculate the percent of Earth's surface that is covered by water.

Fact 1:

Fact 2:

Go on ▶

30 Fiona and Shayla were asked to find the area of a hexagon. Fiona had a good idea. She thought that the hexagon could be divided up into 6 congruent triangles.

- Use your pencil and a straight-edge to divide the hexagon into 6 congruent triangles.

- Label the line segments with the proper lengths.

- Identify any other information you need.

- Briefly explain how this idea could help you find the area of the hexagon.

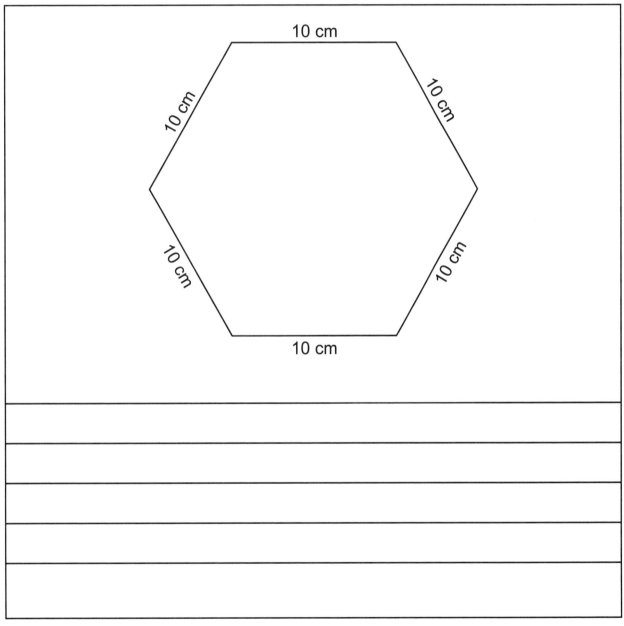

Go on ▶

31 Fiona and Shayla were asked to find the area of a regular hexagon with each side 10 cm long. Shayla thought that the hexagon could be divided up into 4 congruent triangles and a rectangle as shown in Diagram 1 below. She then noticed that if 2 of the triangles were cut out and moved, they would fit together exactly with the other two triangles and form one large rectangle as shown in Diagrams 2 and 3 below.

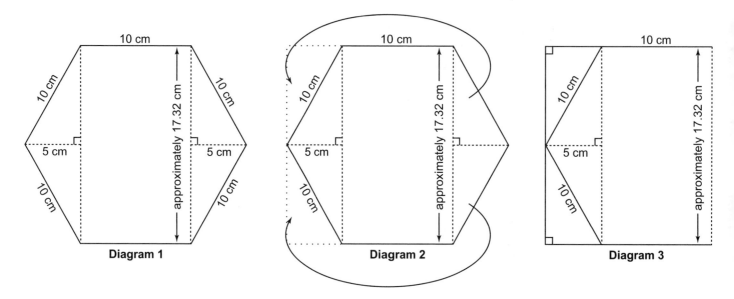

Looking at her sketch, she then reasoned that the area of the hexagon must be approximately 259.8 square centimeters.

If you think Shayla's solution and reasoning are correct, briefly explain how she arrived at her answer and why it represents the area of the hexagon.

If you don't think Shayla's solution and reasoning are correct, briefly explain her mistakes, then calculate the correct answer to the nearest tenth of a square centimeter, and explain your solution.

Go on ▶

Show your work using words, numbers, and/or pictures.

Go on ▶

32 Jake asked nine of his friends how much allowance they received. He arranged his results in a table and took it to his parents.

Name	Duncan	Mary	Robert	James	Paula	Cara	Steven	Andrew	John
$ per week	20	3	5	5	15	2	3	5	5

Since Jake gets $5.00 per week allowance, briefly explain how Jake can use the data in this table to argue that his own allowance should be increased.

Then briefly explain how Jake's parents can use the same data to argue that it should not be increased.

Jake's argument for an increase in his allowance:

Jake's parents' argument for not increasing Jake's allowance:

Go on ▶

33 Jill planted a tree in a windy meadow and she thought it would be wise to attach a guy wire for support. The wire is attached to the tree 8.5 feet above the ground and attached to a stake 14 feet from the base of the tree.

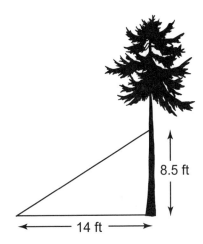

8.5 ft

14 ft

Approximately how long must the wire be?

Explain your answer using the Pythagorean theorem.

The wire must be approximately _____ feet long.

Go on ▶

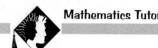
34 This table shows the total number of tropical storms, and those, which became hurricanes, by month, for the period 1851-2004. It also shows the monthly total number of hurricanes to strike the U. S. since 1851.

Total Number of Tropical Storms by Month

Month	Tropical Storms	Hurricanes	U.S. Landfalling Hurricanes
Jan–Apr	5	1	0
May	18	4	0
June	76	28	19
July	94	47	23
August	336	214	74
September	448	309	102
October	273	154	50
November	58	38	5
December	8	4	0

Sources: Atlantic Oceanographic and Meteorological Laboratory (AOML)
National Oceanographic and Atmospheric Administration (NOAA)

What **percentage** of the hurricanes that struck land in the United States since 1851 occurred during the month of September? Explain your answer.

Percentage of hurricanes that struck land in the United States since 1851 that occurred in September is _____.

Go on ▶

Write two other questions that could be answered using the data in the table.

Question 1:

Question 2:

Go on ▶

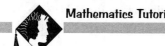

35 A concert promoter is considering renting an 8,000-seat arena and bringing in a rock group to perform. The arena rent costs $10,500, the band costs $12,000, and setup and security cost $8,500. The promoter expects to sell 3,000 tickets at $16.00 each, and there are no other expenses.

How much profit will the promoter make on this arrangement?

Show your work using words, numbers, and/or pictures.

The promoter will make $_____ profit on this arrangement.

STOP

Mathematics Assessment

The Mathematics Assessment is made up of multiple-choice questions, completion items, and short-answer questions. These questions show you how the skills you have learned in Mathematics class may be tested on the Mathematics MSP. The questions also give you a chance to practice your skills. If you have trouble with an area, talk with a parent or teacher.

Read each question carefully. If you do not know an answer, you may skip the question and come back to it later.

When you finish, check your answers.

Directions for Mathematics Assessment

Today you will take the Mathematics Measurements of Student Progress Assessment.

Directions to the Student

There are several different types of questions on this assessment:

1. Some questions will ask you to choose the best answer from among four answer choices. These items are worth one point.

2. Some questions will ask you to write or draw an answer neatly and clearly **inside** an answer box.

    • Some of these questions are short. They may ask you to write a short answer, such as a single number or one or two words. These items are worth one point.

    • Others ask for more details (graphs, tables, written summaries). They may ask you to write an answer, to show how you got your answer using words, numbers, or pictures, or show the steps you used to solve the problem. These questions also provide you with more room for your answer. These items are worth two points.

Here are some important things to remember as you take this assessment:

1. Read each question carefully and think about the answer.

2. When you choose a multiple-choice answer, make sure you completely fill in the circle next to the answer. Erase completely any marks that you want to change on multiple-choice items.

3. When an answer box is provided, write your answer neatly and clearly **inside** the box and show all your work. Cross out any work you do not want as part of your answer. **Do not use scratch paper.**

4. Use only a **No. 2 pencil**, not a mechanical pencil or pen, to write your answers. If you do not have a No. 2 pencil, ask your teacher to give you one.

5. You should have plenty of time to finish every question on the assessment. If you do not know the answer to a question, go on to the next question. You can come back to that question later.

6. When you reach the word **STOP** in your booklet, you have reached the end of the assessment. Do **not** go on until you are told to turn the page.

7. If you finish early, you may check your work in this session **only**.

Go on ▶

     © Englefield & Associates, Inc.

1 Which of the following contains values that are equivalent?

    ○ **A.** $\frac{1}{2}$, 12%, 0.12

    ○ **B.** $\frac{10}{100}$, 1%, 0.10

    ○ **C.** $\frac{5}{25}$, 0.025, 25%

    ○ **D.** $\frac{2}{5}$, 0.4, 40%

2 Ben is reading a book with 200 pages. He reads 17 pages each night. He has already read for "x" nights.

Which equation tells how many pages (p) he has left to read?

    ○ **A.** $p = 200 - 17$

    ○ **B.** $p = 200 - x$

    ○ **C.** $p = 200 - 17x$

    ○ **D.** $p = 200 \div 17x$

Go on ►

3 Ivy and her family celebrated her birthday at her favorite Mexican restaurant. The bill came to $39.00. Since the food and service were excellent, Ivy's dad wanted to leave a 20% tip.

Write how much tip he left.

Ivy's dad left $_____.

4 Which of these charts represents a **proportional relationship**?

○ **A.**

x	1	2	3	4
y	5	6	7	8

○ **B.**

x	1	2	3	4
y	1	4	9	16

○ **C.**

x	1	2	3	4
y	8	6	4	2

○ **D.**

x	1	2	3	4
y	10	20	30	40

Go on ▶

5 Mr. Lee drew this picture for his students and explained to them that any cone fills exactly one-third of the volume of a cylinder in which it fits perfectly. He then asked his students to find the volume of a cone with a diameter of 10 inches and a height of 12 inches.

Use the formula $V_{cone} = \pi r^2 \frac{h}{3}$.

What is the volume of a cone with a diameter of 10 inches and a height of 12 inches?

○ **A.**   125.6 cubic inches

○ **B.**   314 cubic inches

○ **C.**   376.8 cubic inches

○ **D.**   942 cubic inches

Go on ▶

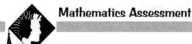
6 Aunt Jean is enlarging her garden. She is doubling the width and tripling the length of the garden.

How can she find how much fencing she will need to go around the garden?

○ **A.** Add the old length and width, then multiply by 5

○ **B.** Add the old length and width, then multiply by 6

○ **C.** Multiply the old width by 4 and multiply the old length by 6, then add the two products

○ **D.** Multiply the length by the width, then double the answer

Go on ▶

© Englefield & Associates, Inc.

7 The following are the scores from Mr. Valenzuela's math class: 75, 80, 65, 70, 70, 85, 90, 95, 90, 85, 90, 80, 85, 90, and 95.

Which of the following bar charts reflects the scores of his class?

 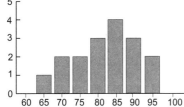

 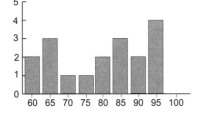

 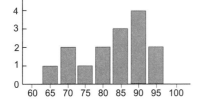

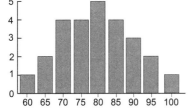

Go on ▶

8 All positive composite numbers can be uniquely written as the product of only prime numbers. This means that there is only one-way to write a given number as the product of primes and no other number shares this same product. The factor tree below shows the number 1,500 factored down to the product of primes. Notice that the two factors of 2 are written with exponents as 2^2 and the three factors of 5 are written with exponents as 5^3.

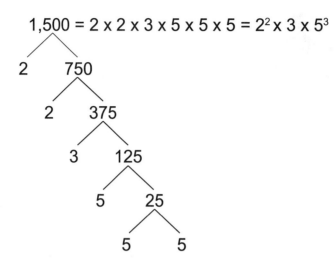

$$1{,}500 = 2 \times 2 \times 3 \times 5 \times 5 \times 5 = 2^2 \times 3 \times 5^3$$

Draw a factor tree of the number 360 in the space below, and use your tree to write 360 as the product of prime numbers. Use exponents to show where it is necessary to show multiple copies of a factor. Show your work using words, numbers, and/or pictures.

Go on ▶

Copying is Prohibited   © Englefield & Associates, Inc.

Draw a factor tree of the number 700 in the space below and use your tree to write 700 as the product of prime numbers. Use exponents to show where it is necessary to show multiple copies of a factor. Show your work using words, numbers, and/or pictures.

Go on ➤

9   Jeremy is given the following graph, and he is told that each square equals one unit.

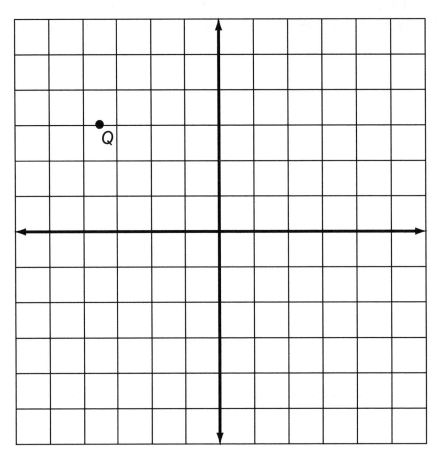

Write the coordinates of point *Q*.

What are the coordinates of point *Q*?_____.

Go on ▶

10 A local apple-growers co-op is packaging apple juice in cylindrical cans. Each can is 8 inches tall and has a diameter of 4.5 inches.

4.5 inch diameter

What is the area of the rectangular label that completely covers the side of the apple-juice can?

○ **A.**   9.42 square inches

○ **B.**   36 square inches

○ **C.**   113.04 square inches

○ **D.**   114 square inches

11 A restaurant receives an order of 54 pounds of choice ribeye steaks priced at $8.75 per pound. The restaurant already owes $562.85 from a previous order. The restaurant manager agrees to pay for the current order as well as the previous balance owed.

Which shows how to find the amount the restaurant manager owes?

○ **A.**   Multiply $8.75 by 54 then add $562.85 to the product

○ **B.**   Multiply $8.75 by 54 then divide $562.85 by the product

○ **C.**   Add $8.75 to $562.85 then multiply the sum by 54

○ **D.**   Add $8.75 to 54 then divide $562.85 by the sum

Go on ▶

12 Which number line illustrates the equation 4 x –2 = –8?

○ **A.**

○ **B.**

○ **C.**
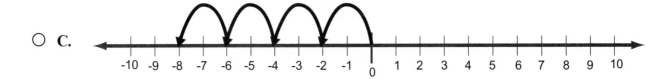

○ **D.**
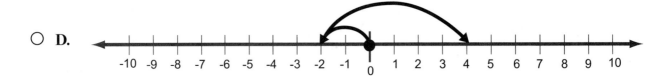

Go on▶

13 Gunter's mom is making mashed potatoes for Thanksgiving dinner. She asks Gunter to go to the store to get her 10 pounds of potatoes. At the store, Gunter weighs one potato and sees it weighs 4.3 ounces. Each potato weighs about the same amount.

Estimate how many potatoes it takes to make a pound (1 pound = 16 ounces). Explain your answer using words, numbers, and/or pictures.

Estimate how many potatoes Gunter should buy for Thanksgiving dinner. Explain your answer using words, numbers, and/or pictures.

About how many potatoes should Gunter buy?_____

Go on ▶

14 Raul and Victor are going camping. The floor of the tent measures 10 feet by 12 feet and the zipper that joins the front flaps is 6 feet long.

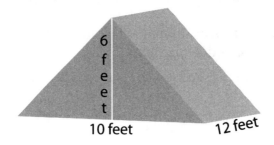

6 feet

10 feet

12 feet

What is the **volume** of the tent?

○ **A.** 120 ft³

○ **B.** 132 ft³

○ **C.** 360 ft³

○ **D.** 720 ft³

Go on ▶

15 Abe flipped a penny five times. Each time, it landed on "heads."

Which of the following statements is **true**?

○ **A.** The next time Abe flips the penny it will most likely land on "heads."

○ **B.** The next time Abe flips the penny it will most likely land on "tails."

○ **C.** The penny will most likely land on "tails" the next 5 times it is flipped.

○ **D.** The next time Abe flips the penny, it has an equal chance of landing on "heads" or "tails."

Go on▶

16 The years of teaching experience among the seventh-grade faculty are shown below.

Teacher	Teaching Experience (Years)
Mr. Hopper	30
Mrs. Delorenzo	16
Mr. Wittum	12
Ms. Baker	10
Mrs. Johnson	26
Mr. Allison	28
Mr. Forte	2
Mr. Jensen	12
Mrs. Elmore	8

What are the mean, median, and range of teaching experience among the seventh-grade faculty? Explain your answer.

What is the mean of teaching experience among the faculty?

Go on ▶

What is the median of teaching experience among the faculty?

Go on▶

17 The students at Lakeview Junior High School were surveyed to determine their favorite season of the year. The table below shows the results.

Lakeview Junior High School

Reply	Percent of Students
Fall	16%
Winter	10%
Spring	9%
Summer	60%
No opinion	5%

Which statement is best supported by this data?

○ **A.** If the students who had no opinion had made a choice among the seasons it would have pushed "Spring" ahead of "Winter."

○ **B.** Many students prefer fall because it is football season.

○ **C.** This survey was taken in summer.

○ **D.** More than twice as many students prefer summer to fall and winter combined.

Go on ▶

© Englefield & Associates, Inc.

18 Pete and Becca own a llama farm. On their farm, they have 240 llamas. Each llama they sell earns them $325.00 profit. They sold 60% of their llamas.

Write how much **total** profit they made.

Pete and Becca made $ _____ in total profit.

19 In the space provided, solve this equation; $7.5x + 32.5 = 94$. Explain your work.

Go on ▶

20 Coach Hare usually runs 13 passing plays out of 40 total plays in a typical football game.

Which proportion could be used to calculate how many passing plays he might be expected to run in a 10-game season?

- ○ **A.** $\frac{13}{40} = \frac{x}{400}$

- ○ **B.** $\frac{13}{40} = \frac{x}{10}$

- ○ **C.** $\frac{13}{10} = \frac{40}{x}$

- ○ **D.** $\frac{13}{40} = \frac{400}{x}$

21 What is the absolute value of –16?

- ○ **A.** –16

- ○ **B.** 4

- ○ **C.** 16

- ○ **D.** 256

Go on ▶

© Englefield & Associates, Inc.

22 In the drawing below, triangle *HIJ* is similar to triangle *KLJ*.

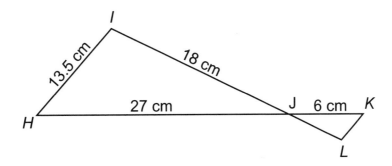

Fill in the table below by listing a segment in triangle *KLJ* that is proportional to the given segment in triangle *HIJ*.

△ HIJ	△ KLJ
HJ	
HI	
IJ	

Set up a proportion and find the lengths of segments *KL, LJ,* and *KJ*.

Go on ►

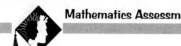
23 The table below shows the hours worked by employees in one week and their weekly pay.

Employees' Hours Worked and Weekly Pay

Employee	Hours	Weekly Pay
Tonya	16	$160
Gary	12	$102
Melissa	20	$190
Vivien	10	$70
Cortez	16	$192

Based on the information in the table, which of the following could **not** be confirmed as true?

○ **A.** Cortez makes more money annually than Melissa makes.

○ **B.** Vivien's hourly wage is less than Gary's hourly wage.

○ **C.** Melissa made more this week than Tonya made.

○ **D.** Cortez's hourly wage is greater than Tonya's hourly wage.

Go on ▶

24 Which model best represents the expression $\frac{1}{2} \times \frac{3}{4}$?

○ **A.**

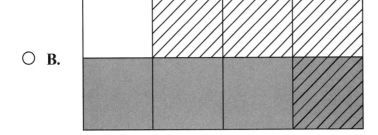

○ **B.**

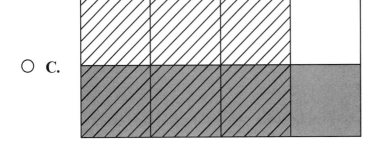

○ **C.**

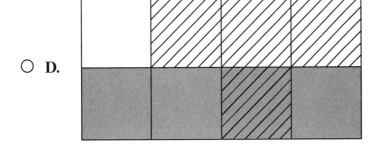

○ **D.**

Go on ➤

25 Conrad is working on a scale model of a historic building, which is $\frac{1}{48}$ the size of the original building. The actual building is 36 feet tall.

How tall is Conrad's model?

    ○ **A.**   2 inches

    ○ **B.**   9 inches

    ○ **C.**   12 inches

    ○ **D.**   22 inches

26 Brady works as an inspector at the Acme Widget Company. During a typical 8 hour day he throws out 68 defective widgets.

How many defective widgets did he find per hour?

    ○ **A.**   6.8

    ○ **B.**   8

    ○ **C.**   8.5

    ○ **D.**   544

Go on ▶

27 Look at the chart below.

Second Die

	1	**2**	**3**	**4**	**5**	**6**
1	1 + 1 = 2	1 + 2 = 3	1 + 3 = 4	1 + 4 = 5	1 + 5 = 6	1 + 6 = 7
2	2 + 1 = 3	2 + 2 = 4	2 + 3 = 5	2 + 4 = 6	2 + 5 = 7	2 + 6 = 8
3	3 + 1 = 4	3 + 2 = 5	3 + 3 = 6	3 + 4 = 7	3 + 5 = 8	3 + 6 = 9
4	4 + 1 = 5	4 + 2 = 6	4 + 3 = 7	4 + 4 = 8	4 + 5 = 9	4 + 6 = 10
5	5 + 1 = 6	5 + 2 = 7	5 + 3 = 8	5 + 4 = 9	5 + 5 = 10	5 + 6 = 11
6	6 + 1 = 7	6 + 2 = 8	6 + 3 = 9	6 + 4 = 10	6 + 5 = 11	6 + 6 = 12

First Die (vertical label for rows)

Which pair of events are **mutually exclusive** in one roll of two standard dice?

○ **A.** Rolling an even number and a number greater than five.

○ **B.** Rolling a double (both dice show the same number) and a number less than five.

○ **C.** Rolling a double (both dice show the same number) and an odd number.

○ **D.** Rolling a double (both dice show the same number) and an even number.

Go on ▶

28 Use the protractor in the diagram to read the measure of each angle.

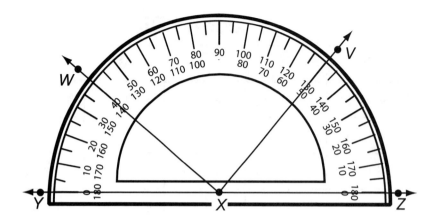

What is one pair of supplementary angles?

○ **A.**   ∠*WXY* and ∠*WXZ*

○ **B.**   ∠*ZXY* and ∠*YXW*

○ **C.**   ∠*YXZ* and ∠*WXV*

○ **D.**   ∠*WXV* and ∠*VXZ*

Go on ▶

29 A group of scouts is splitting the cost of its camping trip evenly. The food costs $23.15. Firewood costs $6.50. The group is spending $17.25 on campsite fees and $27.50 for a canoe rental. Each scout pays $12.40 as his share of the total.

How many scouts are on the camping trip?

○ **A.**   6

○ **B.**   20

○ **C.**   50

○ **D.**   74.4

Go on ▶

30 Sally had a total party budget of $85.00. She spent $15.00 on decorations and bought pizzas for $6.00 each. She wants to determine how much money she has left to spend.

What piece of information is missing for this problem to be solved successfully?

○ **A.**   How much each pizza costs

○ **B.**   How much she spent on decorations

○ **C.**   How many pizzas she bought

○ **D.**   Her total budget

Go on ▶

31 In the scale drawing below, the flagpole is 3 inches high.

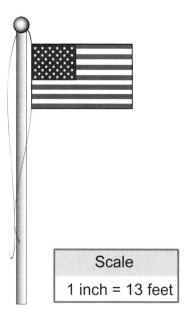

Scale
1 inch = 13 feet

Use the scale in the drawing to find the actual height of the flagpole.

• Write the actual height of the flagpole.

The flagpole's actual height is _____ .

Go on ▶

32 Chocolate candy at the Bon Bon Belle Candy Shoppe costs $14.00 for 4 lbs.

On the graph below draw a line showing the cost for any given amount of chocolate candy from one pound to ten pounds.

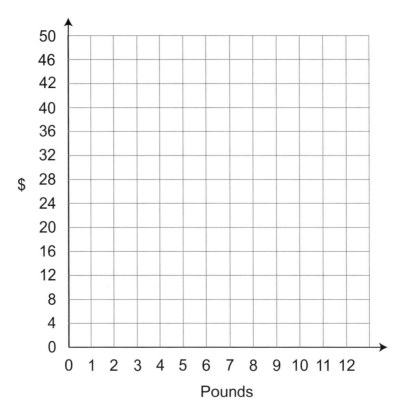

What is the slope of the line on the graph?

The slope of the line is _____.

Go on ▶

     © Englefield & Associates, Inc.

33 Which of these graphs shows the relationship between pints and gallons?

○ **A.**

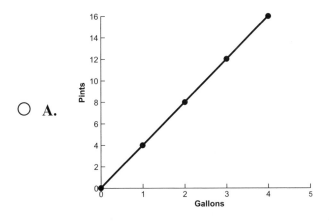

○ **C.**

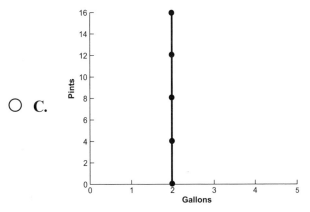

○ **B.**

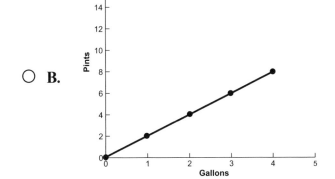

○ **D.**

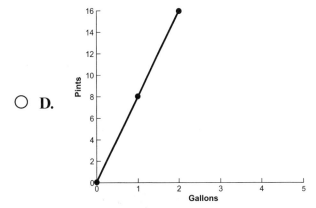

Go on ▶

34 The table below shows the daily high temperatures for one week.

**High Temperatures for
One Week**

Day	High Temp.
Monday	88
Tuesday	86
Wednesday	84
Thursday	88
Friday	80
Saturday	81
Sunday	83

Which graph best represents the information given in the table?

○ **A.**
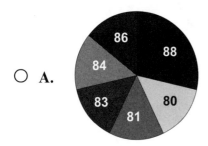

○ **C.**
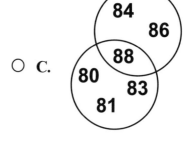

○ **B.**
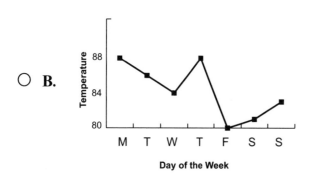

○ **D.**
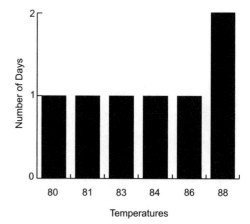

Go on ▶

35 Manuel was throwing a pizza party for his baseball team. He is ordering 12 pizzas and must pay $102 for the entire order. There are a total of 15 players on the team.

Which of the following questions could be answered from the given information?

  ○ **A.**   How much will Manuel tip the delivery person?

  ○ **B.**   How much pizza each team member will eat?

  ○ **C.**   How much will each team member pay?

  ○ **D.**   How much does each pizza cost?

STOP

Notes

Notes

SHOW WHAT YOU KNOW® ON THE MSP FOR GRADE 7, ADDITIONAL PRODUCTS

**For More Information, call our toll-free number: 1.877.PASSING (727.7464)
or visit our website: www.passthemsp.com**